CONTINUOUS HEURISTICS
The Prelinguistic Basis of Intelligence

ELLIS HORWOOD SERIES IN ARTIFICIAL INTELLIGENCE

Joint Series Editors: Professor JOHN CAMPBELL, Department of Computer Science, University College London, and
Dr JEAN HAYES MICHIE, Research Associate, The Turing Institute, Glasgow

CONTINUOUS HEURISTICS
The Prelinguistic Basis of Intelligence

ALEX M. ANDREW B.Sc. (1st class Hons.), Ph.D.
Viable Systems, Chillaton, Devon
and former lecturer in Cybernetics, University of Reading

ELLIS HORWOOD
NEW YORK   LONDON   TORONTO   SYDNEY   TOKYO   SINGAPORE

First published in 1990 by
ELLIS HORWOOD LIMITED
Market Cross House, Cooper Street,
Chichester, West Sussex, PO19 1EB, England
A division of
Simon & Schuster International Group

© Ellis Horwood Limited, 1990

Printed and bound in Great Britain
by Bookcraft (Bath) Limited, Midsomer Norton

British Library Cataloguing in Publication Data

Andrew, Alex M.
Continuous heuristics:
the prelinguistic basis of intelligence. —
(Ellis Horwood series in artificial intelligence).
1. Artificial intelligence
I. Title
006.3
ISBN 0–13–171109–1

Library of Congress Cataloging-in-Publication Data

Andrew, A. M.
Continuous heuristics: the prelinguistic basis of
intelligence / Alex M. Andrew.
p. cm. — (Ellis Horwood series in artificial intelligence)
ISBN 0–13–171109–1
1. Artificial intelligence. I. Title. II. Series.
Q335.A583   1990
006.3–dc20   89–24499
                                              CIP

Contents

Preface ix

1 Artificial Intelligence and Continuity
1.1 An impasse in AI 1
1.2 Emergence of AI 3
1.3 Learning 5
1.4 Continuity 7
1.5 Evolution 1 10
1.6 Evolution 2 13
1.7 Robotics 13
1.8 Heuristics 14
1.9 Background 17
1.10 Overview of the other chapters 22

2 Evident Continuity
2.1 Introduction 25
2.2 Analog and digital computing 25
2.3 Induction 27
2.4 Nonmonotonic reasoning 28
2.5 Fuzzy set theory and other bridges 30
2.6 Pattern classification 33
2.7 Self-optimization 35
2.8 Odd and even objective functions 35
2.9 Internal models 38
    2.9.1 Error decorrelation 39
    2.9.2 Samuel's learning algorithm 40
    2.9.3 Perceptrons 41
2.10 Learning filters 42
2.11 Self-organization 43
    2.11.1 Pandemonium 45
    2.11.2 Janet 46
    2.11.3 Significance feedback 47
    2.11.4 Selection strategies 49
    2.11.5 Alternative formulations 50
    2.11.6 Self-organization and evolution 52
2.12 Daisyworld 52

3 Hidden Continuity

3.1 Where continuity lurks 56

3.2 Neural network models 56

   3.2.1 Continuity in neural nets 61

3.3 State-determined bahaviour 63

   3.3.1 Automaton theory 64

3.4 The Ashby-Bellman debate 65

3.5 Analogy 66

   3.5.1 Heuristic connection 67

   3.5.2 Types of similarity 68

3.6 Language and jokes 73

4 Evolution

4.1 The concept of a concept 76

4.2 Succinctness 78

4.3 Goals and meta-goals 79

   4.3.1 Persistence in evolution 81

   4.3.2 Remarks on neural coding 83

4.4 The emergence of concepts 85

   4.4.1 Evolution of communication 88

5 Continuous Heuristics

5.1 The argument 91

   5.1.1 Minsky's argument 92

   5.1.2 Other arguments 92

5.2 A speeding-up robot 93

   5.2.1 Robot path control 94

   5.2.2 Geometric reasoning 96

   5.2.3 Motion heuristics 96

   5.2.4 Representations 99

5.3 A relevant experiment 103

   5.3.1 Digital simulation 104

   5.3.2 Simplified scheme 104

5.4 Automatic optimization 106

   5.4.1 Rosenbrock's method 110

   5.4.2 Optimizing a trajectory 112

   5.4.3 Heuristic extension 115

5.5 Results 117

   5.5.1 Rosdal 117

   5.5.2 Rosderiv 119

   5.5.3 Comparison with manual adjustment 119

6 Conclusions
   6.1 Introspection on continuity.....................................121
   6.2 Relevance of robotics 122
   6.3 Where now?...122
   6.4 Palaeo-AI 125
   6.5 Finally 126

References...127

Appendix A   Pascal Programs
   A.1 Main optimization program 141
   A.2 Rosderiv 153
   A.3 Rosdual..165

Appendix B   The Gram-Schmidt Method
   B.1 The method 172

Index..173

To Joyce

Preface

In the course of setting down these diverse arguments and viewpoints, it has been impossible not to swing between two opposite feelings about the project. Sometimes it seemed like an unwarranted attack on the well-established and successful field of AI. At other times it appeared to be so obvious as to verge on tautology, and in any case it seemd that the ground had been well-covered by MacKay and Minsky and others. McCorduck's book (1979) gives a very fair and thoughtful review of attitudes on the place of continuity.

Of course, a great deal hinges on what is understood by *Artificial Intelligence*. Sometimes the term is used to refer to an established body of theory and techniques rather than to the general problem of understanding and simulating human intelligence. The body of theory and techniques has been developed in the attempt to model certain features of human performance, and there can be little doubt about its power and relevance within this restricted area of application. It has been remarked that the special programming languages of AI become so 'natural' to their users that there must be some deep correspondence between the information structures of the languages and those of the brain.

Some workers like to preserve the 'purity' of this retrospective view of AI, and to claim that *robotics* is not truly part of it. Such a view preserves the internal consistency of the subject-area, but the main argument of this book is that it is intrinsically inadequate.

To argue about attitudes and approaches is to engage in the dangerous activity of making broad generalizations. One reason for the above-mentioned ambiguity of feelings about the treatment here is that attitudes are rapidly changing in the AI field. There has been, in the past, an unfortunate and counter-productive dogmatism about respective approaches, but there are signs that this is disappearing. Nevertheless, there is still disagreement about the place of continuity.

The idea that human thought is primarily 'logical' in a sense that excludes continuity, is older than AI, and this book is essentially an attempt to examine the validity and consequences of this assumption and to consider alternatives. The idea could be held to be refuted by the simple observation that many words of natural language refer to attributes that may exist in varying degrees. There is a tendency, when discussing *concepts* in the abstract, to form a mental picture of a concept as corresponding to a class of physical objects, like the concept of a dog or a man or a bicycle. However, language has many words denoting concepts that are less easily visualized and have a continuous character, even though the attributes they represent may or may not be precisely quantifiable.

Some examples in the English language are beauty, intransigence, compatability, integrity, and others can be found on any page of the dictionary.

There are many reasons for believing that concept-based thought is influenced by little-understood continuous processes operating subconsciously. It has presumably evolved from primitive processing in which continuity was evident. It is therefore useful to think of its continuous aspects as a legacy from the earlier processing, rather than as a fresh development, and this has implications for AI in general. It is argued that the needs of advanced robotics will force these considerations into the open. A study of a simple manipulative task is discussed in support of this.

The presentation has been greatly improved by giving consideration to comments by the Series Editor, Prof. John Campbell, whom I thank for his help. In places, especially the last two chapters, his comments have prompted changes that go beyond the details of the presentation, and have materially improved the coherence of the whole treatment. Nevertheless, responsibility for errors and residual lack of coherence, and for the views expressed, is my own.

The presentation has also been enormously improved, as has that of everything else I have written in the last thirty-odd years, by the collaboration of my wife, Joyce.

Alex. M. Andrew

1

Artificial Intelligence and Continuity

1.1 AN IMPASSE IN AI

Although work under the heading of 'Artificial Intelligence' has produced positive and useful results, it has also shown that the achievement of something to warrant description as 'artificial intelligence' is more difficult than was once supposed. To say this is to gloss over questions of definition of terms (of 'intelligence' itself, for a start), but most people would agree that the intelligence of machines is still, in some intangible way, qualitatively different from that of living systems.

In discussing human attitudes it is important to remember that criteria are influenced by what is known to have been achieved. The very fact that some result has been obtained in an artifact makes it unlikely that it will be accepted as a demonstration of 'intelligence'. Even allowing for this, though, there seems to be a wide gap between machine and brain performance.

Some philosophers argue that human and machine intelligence are fundamentally different and that the capabilities of machines must inevitably lag behind those of brains in some respects. This question will probably never be settled and is perhaps more a matter of religion than of science. I have found no good reason to refute what Searle (1984) terms the "strong AI position", according to which there is no *essential* difference between human and machine intelligence. To say this is not to deny that there are features of human intelligence that are currently highly mysterious.

The debate as to whether there are *ultimate* intrinsic limitations on AI achievement is somewhat academic, especially as it is difficult to imagine what discovery or development would be universally accepted as settling it. The assertion here is that AI is at an impasse because there are aspects of intelligence

1

we do not sufficiently understand. This is not to suggest they cannot usefully be investigated.

Recent years have seen enthusiasm for 'expert systems' as the main growing-point of AI. Many introductory and review texts seemed almost to equate the whole field of AI to the development and use of expert systems. Certainly, there are sound practical reasons for developing this particular subdivision of the subject-area. Expert systems have proved their worth in connection with medical diagnosis and training, and in a wide range of other applications they are useful and economically viable. These considerations are particularly significant in times of financial stringency. In Britain, attitudes are still slightly coloured by a desire to refute the contention of the Lighthill Report (Science Research Council 1973) that AI is an esoteric and useless area of study.

The purpose of an expert system is essentially that of AI itself, namely to model some fraction of human intelligence in a machine. However, the result is achieved by setting up a standard framework which can be seen either as a set of unwarranted assumptions about the nature of the thought process or simply as an arbitrary structure having enough adjustable parameters to ensure that an approximate match can be formed with a wide variety of prototypes. In the latter interpretation it resembles the procedure of regression analysis (see, for example, Draper and Smith 1966) for forming a model of a physical process. Often a model can be found which has predictive value and serves practical purposes, but the process of fitting it has given no insight into the underlying mechanisms of the process modelled.

Limitations of the expert-system approach are acknowledged by Rich (1983) who makes the following comment (p. 291):

(a) "These systems derive their power from a great deal of domain-specific knowledge, rather than from a single powerful technique."

(b) "The required knowledge is about a particular area and is well-defined. This contrasts with the kind of broad, hard-to-define knowledge that we call common sense. It is easier to build expert systems than ones with common sense."

There are, of course, expert systems of different kinds, some modelling the physical characteristics of the domain of expertise in a deeper way than by holding a list of production rules (de Kleer 1984; Fischler and Firschein 1987). These may be exempted from the criticism illustrated by comparison with regression analysis, but presumably at the cost of increased domain specificity. The term *expert system* is not precisely defined, and tends to be loosely applied to any system that can be held to imitate human expertise. The intention here, and in the critical remarks of Rich, is to restrict the interpretation to systems using a particular set of techniques outlined, for example, in a state-of-the-art review by Buchanan (1982).

If AI has indeed come to an impasse, or even if progress is just slower than we feel it should be, we obviously want to look for what is missing in the approach. It has often been suggested that an important missing ingredient is *learning*. The kind of learning visualized is that allowing acquisition of skill rather than of data; the idea is that the program should learn from experience how to perform tasks, or at least that it should improve its quality of performance as it gains experience. As will be seen, the distinction between skill and data acquisition may not be sharp. Before discussing the implications of this it is interesting to recall some of the early history of AI.

1.2 EMERGENCE OF AI

In some form or another, the idea that artifacts might duplicate or at least imitate a part of human intelligent activity is quite old. A number of writers, such as George and Humphries (1974), McCorduck (1979) and Fischler and Firschein (1987) have reviewed early expressions of the idea. George and Humphries are able to refer to the *Iliad*, and to Indian legends, for early descriptions of free-moving intelligent robots. The Bible makes reference to *teraphim*, apparently figures or heads used for divination in a pagan religion (usually termed *idols* or *images* in English translation), and some representations of these show them as robot-like. Later on, the idea found expression in the mechanical head reputedly built by Roger Bacon (1214–1292) and in a wealth of automata devised in the eighteenth century. At least one of these was purported to be a chess-playing machine, though it is now known to have been a fake.

Apart from these efforts, and other speculations referring to flesh-and-blood creations such as that of Frankenstein, there was another path of development of relevant ideas, of a more philosophical nature. Descartes (1596–1650) postulated communication through nerve tubes in the body and hence a mechanism playing some part in intelligent behaviour. The construction of a calculating machine by Pascal demonstrated that certain mental activites could be performed mechanic-ally, and each of Leibnitz, Boole and Ada Lovelace explicitly visualized either mechanisms or formal mathematical methods to duplicate human reasoning.

Many of the eighteenth-century automata imitate human movement fairly well, but their information-processing capability is limited. Developments in electronics, particularly during the Second World War, indicated that artifacts displaying much more interesting behaviour were a distinct possibility. This was clear even before general-purpose digital computers were widely available, especially when the new techniques were applied to the experimental study of the nervous system including the brain. The invention of several types of microelectrode made it a reasonably simple matter to record the activity of single nerve cells, and also to apply highly localized stimuli. There was then the possibility, in principle, of analysing the activity of the brain in much the same way as one would examine the operation of a piece of electronic equipment.

We can now see that the application of these techniques has produced an enormous increase in understanding of the working of the brain, especially concerning the early stages of processing of sensory data, but this hardly scratches the surface of the overall problem of understanding the mechanisms underlying thought. In the early days (i.e. the nineteen-forties and early fifties) the magnitude of the problem tended to be underestimated, and most of the speculation about achieving intelligence in artifacts was on the assumption that the best way to set about it was to build networks of elements having properties resembling those of the nerve cells (neurons) of the brain. The scene was largely set by the famous paper of McCulloch and Pitts (1943). This showed that a simple type of model neuron was a universal computing element, in that any computable function could be realized in a network of such elements.

In this initial analysis McCulloch and Pitts considered networks of elements with fixed properties; they did not introduce any form of *neural plasticity* which might allow self-organization and learning. However, they expressed their interest in such further developments of their work. It has in fact been said that Walter Pitts was working on a powerful theory related to a mechanism of self-organization but never brought it to a stage where he was prepared to publish it. Some form of self-organization, implying neural plasticity, was a feature of the many schemes for achieving intelligent behaviour from neural nets.

These early speculations and studies under the heading of *cybernetics* can be seen as the beginning of AI in the modern scientific context. It was realized in the late nineteen-fifties that intelligence also had to be studied in a global or macroscopic way that was difficult to relate to phenomena at the single-cell level. At this time the term *artificial intelligence* was devised and workers in the new subject area explicitly rejected any restriction to a neural net or any other specific type of model. Associated with this was a de-emphasis of *learning* as an aspect of the systems studied; some sort of plasticity which could be loosely termed 'learning' was a feature of most neural-net schemes, but the new approach could produce interesting effects without explicitly invoking it.

It is interesting to note, however, that in recent years there has been a revival of interest in neural nets. There are various reasons for this, among them being hardware developments allowing implementation of the networks with efficiency many orders of magnitude greater than that of their simulation on serial machines. Apart from this, however, a paper by Hopfield (1982) is widely accepted as providing the theoretical breakthrough that allows neural nets to be applied to tasks beyond the image pre-processing level of sophistication. From the point of view of the argument of this book it is significant that Hopfield departs from the McCulloch-Pitts approach by treating neurons as *continuous* elements. This is discussed in more detail in Chapter 3.

Freed from the restrictions to which earlier workers had subjected themselves, and benefiting from the ever-increasing power and availability of computers, AI work took off impressively. Because it produces new challenges, and has an intrinsic fascination which has attracted many able minds to work on it, it has formed a spearhead of progress in computer science. Forsyth and Naylor (1985) have summed this up by describing AI as the "department of clever tricks" of computer science. However, with a few exceptions, notably the checker-playing program due to Samuel (1963) and various schemes for pattern recognition, the programs that could be said to break new ground in the early development of AI could not be said to learn from experience. Of those which did embody a learning capability, the changes which could result from learning were within a very restricted domain of possibilities.

The development of non-learning AI programs constitutes a learning process undertaken by the programmer and computer jointly. Since the main, or 'clever', component comes from the human it is easy to feel, as Selfridge and Neisser (1963) put it, that the machine intelligence is "strongly tainted with artifice". This is a subjective and imprecise argument since a certain amount of such 'taint' is inevitable in any system which does not duplicate the whole process of biological evolution. Nevertheless if a program does not autonomously learn from experience the taint of artifice is stronger than we would like.

1.3 LEARNING

The idea of 'learning', however, is like that of 'intelligence' in resisting precise definition. It is easy to say that the emphasis is on skill acquisition rather than data acquisition, but the distinction between the two is not necessarily clear. We do not say that a tape recorder has learned something when a song or poem is recorded (even though a child is credited with learning ability for having done essentially the same thing). The difficulty of making the distinction becomes evident in connection with expert systems. New facts acquired by such programs are most readily thought of as data, but may influence performance in what seems to be a qualitative way. In a simpler way the same is true of most non-trivial programs, since arrangements for *conditional jumps* are a feature of all machine languages (and are carried over to high-level ones as IF and WHILE constructions), and they allow computed or inserted values to influence the sequence of operations. In fact, one of the remarkable ways in which Babbage and Lady Lovelace were ahead of their time was in appreciating the need for conditionals.

A useful definition of learning requires a distinction between qualitative and quantitative changes in behaviour, and this cannot be made precise. The difficulty is discussed by Rich (1983) using arguments similar to the above. Schank (1985) reviews the history of attitudes to learning during the history of AI. For many years it was deprecated as a research topic, mainly because there seemd to be no good way of getting to grips with it. In recent years it has gained respectability, but with a somewhat different viewpoint. Within its own terms of reference the new viewpoint represents an advance in understanding, but insistence on these terms can be seen as a trick by which the topic is trimmed down to fit traditional AI frameworks.

There is, in fact, a problem in defining any term denoting self-modification of an entity. Such terms include *learning, self-organization* and *adaptation*. Any definition of a process of self-modification requires an arbitrary division of the internal information of the entity into that which defines it and that which is seen as data passing through. An alternative way of expressing this is to say that there has to be an arbitrary decision about how much of the entity's history is accepted as the stimulus producing the response. If a sufficiently large portion is regarded as the stimulus, changes that would otherwise be accepted as constituting learning come to be interpreted as representations of data passing through.

This question of definition has received attention in connection with *self-organizing systems* (Andrew 1989). The difficulty becomes apparent when it is considered that a computer program running on a machine is a finite automaton (Minsky 1967) and can therefore, in principle, be represented in the formalism of automaton theory. That is to say, it can be defined by specifying a set of possible states and another of possible inputs and then, for each possible pairing of a state with an input, indicating an output (which may be null) and a next state.

Since states may differ in only one binary digit of storage, the number of them to be listed is likely to be vast and unmanageable, but in principle any program can be represented in this way.

Even if the program is one which, viewed in a different way, is readily acknowledged as being able to learn, its finite-automaton description is unaltered by the learning process. If restarted from a given base state it would produce the same outputs from the same total sequence of inputs. If, then, the total sequence of inputs is held to determine an output there is no evidence for learning. There is, however, evidence for learning if an output is considered to be a response to only a small immediately-preceding part of the history of inputs.

Because of the difficulties of definition, a reference to the lack of learning capability is not a clear indication of a missing ingredient in AI. It will be argued here that a more useful way of indicating a missing ingredient is to refer to the need to exploit *continuity* (in a special sense of the word discussed in the next section) in AI programs. At first sight this seems to be a jump to a totally different aspect, but in fact there is a close connection between learning and continuity. The two ideas are intricately interwoven.

1.4 CONTINUITY

The importance of a form of continuity is tacitly acknowledged in a great deal of discussion in AI. Minsky (1959b, 1963) has introduced it explicitly as *heuristic connection* between problems. He introduces the idea informally, simply as "some additional structure on the search space". He believes it is unprofitable to invoke mathematical theory associated with the ideas of *metric* or *topology*, even though the use of these terms is invited by reference to *connection* and hence to *distance* as its inverse.

Essentially the same idea occurs in various discussions, e.g. that of Carbonell (1984). He comments that it is rare for a person to encounter a problem that bears no relation to other ones solved or observed in past experience, so it is at least as important to consider how the thinking process slides from problem to problem as it is to decide how a problem of a totally new kind would be tackled. He is, of course, referring to the use of *analogy* in problem-solving, which is currently receiving much attention.

An earlier paper by Minsky and Selfridge (1961) expressed the same idea in their *basic learning heuristic*, as a preliminary to discussion of problem-solving as hill-climbing. At first sight the *heuristic* seems too obvious to be worth stating, but on consideration it is seen to be an explicit recognition of the value of analogy. The assertion is as follows:

> "In a novel situation try methods like those that have worked best in similar situations."

Two forms of undefined similarity are involved, namely similarity of situation and similarity of method. One way of recognizing similarities is to group siutations, or methods, into categories, and as these authors say:

> "... advanced forms [of learning] which discover and use new categories can cover the creative aspects of genius."

The meaning that can usefully be attached to *continuity* in this context is not the same as mathematical continuity. The latter is defined by saying that a function $f(x)$ is continuous at a if its limit, as $x \to a$, is $f(a)$. In AI we are more interested in continuity 'in the large', such that interpolation and extrapolation, and ranking and distance comparison, have meaning. This kind of continuity can exist for variates that can take only discrete values. For example, the integers are discontinuous in the mathematical sense, and so are reals as represented digitally in a computer.

MacKay, as quoted by McCorduck (1979), indicated the importance of interpolation by saying (p. 79):

> "... a digital computer is unable to represent the concept of in between."

He could have extended the comment to extrapolation by also including the concept of beyond. He is, I think, mistaken in contrasting analog and digital computers; the constrast is between digital computers performing logical operations and computing methods that recognize continuity 'in the large'.

It might have been better to avoid confusion by using some other word to refer to continuity 'in the large', but the word 'continuity' seems intuitively right. Berliner (1985) uses the term *quasi-continuity* to refer to a similar idea, and suggests that a quasi-continuous criterion should be held to exist when 30 or more members of a set can be ranked.

The importance of continuity was recognized in early discussions by MacKay (1959) with an emphasis slightly different from that of Minsky and Selfridge. Essentially the same viewpoint as that of the *basic learning heuristic* has been put forward by Lenat (1984) in discussing evolution. As he neatly expresses it:

> "Appropriateness(action, situation) is a continuous function."

He has also been able to link the ideas to no less an authority than Poincaré, whom he quotes as saying:

> "The whole idea of analogy is that 'Effects', viewed as a function of situation, is a continuous function."

The representation of problem-solving as hill-climbing clearly assumes continuity. Minsky and Selfridge introduce the *basic learning heuristic* as a preliminary to this and go on to show that the hill-climbing process may come to a halt because of what they term the *mesa phenomenon*. That is to say, the operating point may reach a flat region of the response surface or 'hill'. They claim that most schemes for self-organizing networks as models of non-trivial learning are bound to fail because of this effect.

A variety of continuous criteria, including *utility estimates* and *difficulty estimates* are needed in the heuristic *administrative methods* discussed by Minsky (1959a). No doubt the thinking which led to enunciation of the *basic learning heuristic* was influenced by Selfridge's earlier discussion of his *pandemonium* scheme (Selfridge 1959). This has a variable number of *computational demons* corresponding roughly to the *feature detectors* of other recognition schemes, or the *hidden units* referred to by Hinton (1989). Two methods were suggested for the creation of new *computational demons*, one of them being by *mutated fission* of other demons that had proved to have high *worth*. In order that the mutations should be potentially useful to the overall performance of the system, the representation of computational demons in this way must involve a suitable form of continuity. The creation of useful demons is in fact an evolutionary process to which the already-mentioned arguments of Lenat (1984) apply.

These arguments for the importance of continuity in intelligent mechanisms may seem, in retrospect, to be simple and rather obvious. On the other hand they represent a departure from traditional logic, which is essentially discrete. Much work in AI is explicityly based on the various forms of *predicate calculus* or systems of formal logic. In computer technology, the term *logic* is used to make a distinction from *arithmetic*, the difference being essentially that the *logical* device or operation can be described without reference to continuity. (This is, of course, continuity in the extended sense introduced here, since computer arithmetic is not continuous in the mathematical sense.)

This restricted interpretation of *logic* is misleading if the word is assumed to have one of its possible dictionary meanings, as the 'science of thinking'. Dictionaries usually qualify the definition by indicating that the reference is especially to thinking that is regular, effective, or scientific. The implication is that the word denotes, not all forms of thinking that might interest a pshychologist, but the restricted area sometimes also denoted by *ratiocination*. There is a widespread and unwarranted assumption, among philosophers and AI workers, that ratiocination is somehow more fundamental than other forms of thought. As discussed in section 1.5, it is possible to find reasons for accepting it as more *laudable* than other forms of thought as a determinant of human discourse, but that is a different issue.

This unwarranted assumption has produced a particular bias in attempts to explain and model thought processes. The tendency is to start by modelling ratiocination, and then to modify the model when its deficiencies become apparent. The restriction to one starting-point is similar to the assumption among mathematicians that the integers or natural numbers are indeed 'natural' and that any theory of mathematics must start with them and then operate on them to produce, first rational numbers, and then irrational ones, and so on.

A great deal of confusion has arisen, both prior to the advent of digital computers and subsequently, because of a failure to distinguish the disparate implications of the word *logic*. In the sense which will be referred to as sense A, it implies the manipulation of discrete values without, at least at the level of axioms and fundamental operations, any regard to continuity. This meaning has been very firmly adopted in the terminology of computer technology. In its other sense, which will be referred to as sense B, it is the *science of thinking*, or at least of effective thinking.

This criticism of the basic assumptions of AI is, of course, painted with a broad brush. There are different schools of thought within AI, and in a recent book called *Logical Foundations of Artificial Intelligence* (Genesereth and Nilsson 1987) the authors make it clear, both by their choice of title and in the notes on the dust-cover, that they approach AI "from the standpoint of logic". The word 'logic' is obviously intended in sense A. The fact that these authors find it necessary to indicate this standpoint amounts to an acknowledgement that others are possible, and hence that 'logic' in sense B is not restricted to its meaning in sense A.

In a more general review of the subject area, Fischer and Firschein (1987) compare, in their *epilogue*, different views of the nature of representation in the brain, and hence of the representation appropriate to AI. They quote Nilsson as a champion of a "logiclike propositional formalism", where, again, 'logic' must be intended in sense A. This formalism is contrasted with theories requiring *iconic* representations, i.e. representations that are like pictures in mapping physical reality.

The reference to iconic representations implies the possibility of continuous deformations, so the distinction corresponds approximately to the continuous/discrete one discussed here. In general, however, there is remarkable reluctance to deviate from guidelines laid down by the ancient Greeks, particularly Aristotle, which encourage the idea that 'logic' in sense A is fundamental to sense B. A possible partial explanation for this can be found by considering the evolution of intelligence.

1.5 EVOLUTION 1

Ashby insisted that the brain should be seen as a 'specialized organ of survival' and from an evolutionary point of view this can seem rather obvious. Sherrington, the 'Father of Neurophysiology', is said (see Andrew 1987a,b) to have remarked that the brain, and hence all mental activity, should be regarded as a development of motor control, i.e. of the means of controlloing muscular activity. A similar idea is expressed by Szentàgothai and Arbib (1975) who give, as the first of five principles for a theory of neural function:

"Theory must be action-oriented".

According to this viewpoint, primitive nervous systems, or mechanisms for information processing that were forerunners of nervous systems, were very much concerned with continuous phenomena. Motor control must involve continuous movements, and the goals determining it were presumably associated with such continuous environmental variables as temperature and the respective concentrations of nutrients and of noxious substances.

In some of the AI literature (e.g. Berliner 1985) there is consideration of the question whether it is better to regard the brain as being programmed procedurally or declaratively. There can be little doubt that primitive nervous systems are essentially procedural. Higher nervous systems have evolved features that may warrnat description as *declarative* in that they seem to provide an explicit model of the environment. The distinction cannot be a sharp one, since it can be shown (Andrew 1967a) that the behaviour of a system using a model may be indistinguishable from that of a system not explicitly model-based. This raises the difficult question af what is to be understood as a 'model'; any system that has evolved so as to achieve some goal in a particular environment must somehow mirror, in its evolved state, the significant features of the environment It is a matter of subjective judgement whether this mirroring is appropriately described as a 'model'.

From its origins as a largely continuous-acting controller the nervous system has evolved both to form internal representations that compellingly invite descriptions as models, and to manipulate discrete concepts. Some of the ways of doing the latter are captured in traditional logic. It is a superior capacity for 'logical' thought (in sense A of the last section) that distinguishes humans from other animals and has allowed the development of science, technology, AI and so on. However, in ways that we do not understand, this progress all depends on the earlier methods evolved for continuous processing, which are presumably still effective in the part of the thought process not accessible to consciousness.

It is perhaps natural that man's image of himself, as embodied in traditional logic, should stress the recent evolutionary developments and associated intellectual achievements, with a failure to realize that these are underpinned by earlier ones. There is a certain parallel with man's image of himself as master of his terrestrial environment, which, if Lovelock (1979) is right in his *Gaia Hypothesis*, ignores the fact that our continued occupancy of the earth depends on regulatory processes involving such lowly creatures as micro-organisms and algae.

Our traditional high regard for *ratiocination* stems partly from its correspondence to traditional logic, and also from the fact that it satisfies evolved subgoals of conciseness and consistency.

It is well known that parts of the nervous system are concerned with processing continuous information. Motor control is a requirement in higher animals just as it is in lower ones, and the performance of acts of skill, like running to catch a ball, must depend on such processing with rather impressive accuracy. Apart from this there are parts of the nervous system which must operate on continuous data in order to regulate internal variables such as body temperature and various aspects of blood chemistry, or the amount of light energy falling on the retinas.

To think of continuous processing as more primitive than the conceptual kind conflicts with the already-mentioned deep-seated idea that 'logic', in sense A, is fundamental. At least, the ideas conflict if it is assumed that 'primitive' implies 'fundamental', in accordance with an evolutionary viewpoint. On the other hand, some comments in the AI literature, such as Minsky's viewpoint on the place of robotics as discussed in Chapter 5, seem to equate 'primitive' with "*not* of fundamental interest for our purposes".

As noted earlier, a similar conflict is associated with the usual assumption in mathematics that the natural numbers are in some sense fundamental or God-given and that ingenuity has to be exercised to fill the gaps between them with, first, rational numbers and then others. It has been suggested, at least informally, by Thom, the pioneer of *catastrophe theory*, that it might be more useful to think of continuous variates as fundamental and to consider how the natural numbers came to be appreciated.

The nature of mental representations has been considered by philosophers, including Descartes and Boole, already mentioned, and notably Hume, as reviewed by Gaines (1977). Through all these discussions there is an explicit or implicit assumption that thought is 'logical' in sense A.

At one stage of his education, Warren McCulloch (1960, 1974) was asked what was to be his life's work, and replied that he wanted to study the question:

> "What is a man that he may know a number, and a number, that a man may know it".

He was told, rightly, that this would keep him busy all his life. The concept of a number is not something to be accepted without further thought as fundamental, but is the result of an evolutionary process. It is part of the general readiness of the nervous system to operate in terms of discrete concepts. Like any particular concept, this general readiness is a result of evolution and has survived because it is useful. An attempt has been made (Andrew 1981) to capture this idea by referring to the *concept of a concept*.

Certainly, the assumption that human thought is essentially 'logical' arose well before there was any idea of biological evolution. George Boole lived from 1815 to 1864, so was contemporaneous with Darwin (1809–1882), but although he produced his famous formalization of what he termed the *laws of thought*, the underlying assumption about the nature of thought is much older. There is a need to reconsider these assumptions in the light of modern ideas about evolution.

1.6 EVOLUTION 2

Evolution itself depends on continuity, since evolutionary steps must traverse some continuum. There has to be some criterion according to which an offspring is similar to its parent or parents, and yet slightly different from them in order to allow evolutionary development. Reference has already been made to the arguments of Lenat (984) indicating the need to consider continuity in connection with evolutionary processes.

1.7 ROBOTICS

One of the reasons for believing tha the nervous systems of higher animals must process continuous data is the need for suitable control of muscular movements. Associated with this is the need to represent the physical environment and to interpret sensory inputs. These requirements are also encountered in the attempt to build autonomous robots. If Sherrington is correct in his view of the evolutionary origin of the brain, it is reasonable to suppose that insights into the basic mechanisms of intelligence may come from work on robots.

That robotics, and its associated problems of perception, require information-processing of a kind that is unfamiliar to workers in traditional AI is acknowledged by Brady (1981):

"Many observations about the world, as well as our assumptions about it, are naturally articulated in terms of 'smoothness' of some appropriate quantity. This intuitive idea is made mathematically precise in a number of ways; in real analysis, for example in conditions for differentiability. Relationships between smoothly varying quantities give rise to differential equations ... "

There is here an appreciation of the need to process continuous information, though it is described as corresponding to mathematical continuity 'in the small' rather than to continuity 'in the large' as emphasized here. In the everyday activities of people and animals, which we would like robots to imitate, there is a complex interaction of the continuous and conceptual kinds of processing.

People seem to take particular pleasure in engaging in activities in which these types of processing are closely interwoven. Such activities include all the games in which balls or similar objects ae thrown, kicked, batted or otherwise propelled, either in areas large enough to hold the players themselves or in restricted ones such as the top of a billiard table. Arcade computer games mostly have the same character. It is as though people realize they have a special facility for combining the two forms with such intimacy and take pleasure in developing and exhibiting it.

Existing robots do not combine the two types of processing with any intimacy. Movement planning is usually done without regard to dynamics, and then the plans are effected by stiff servo-mechanisms. The planning process requires a combination of discrete and continuous processing, but not in a close way with on-line interaction between the two.

The result of the separation between planning and servo-control is that robots conforming to it are slow and energeticaly inefficient, and are not readily able to operate in an environment where the objects to be manipulated are themselves moving ballistically. The need for a unified treatment in the latter situation is illustrated by work on walking machines, especially bipeds (Raibert 1984, 1985; Hamami and Zheng 1984; Borovac, Vukobratović and Surla 1989).

1.8 HEURISTICS

Almost all work in AI embodies an explicit departure from strictly 'logical' (in sense A) inference or *ratiocination*. The use of *heuristics* is fundamental to most AI work, to such an extent that the term *heuristic programming approach* has been used (Slagle 1971) to distinguish what is now generally understood simply by 'AI' from the alternative based on neural nets and self-organization.

The term *heuristic* is defined by Feigenbaum and Feldman (1963) as follows:

> "A *heuristic (heuristic rule, heuristic method)* is a rule of thumb, simplification, or any other kind of device which drastically limits search for solutions in large problem [more correctly, solution] spaces."

It is, of course, to be understood that the reference to 'limiting' the search is not meant to indicate constraints on it that would render it less effective. The idea is that the search is guided by heuristic principles so as to be likely to be successful with less effort expended.

Proverbs can be thought of as heuristics for everyday living. For example, we have "Honesty is the best policy" and "Waste not, want not". Most people would agree that, while these are good rules to follow most of the time, they do not always 'work' ('White lies' can be valuable in smoothing relationships; costs of repair and maintenance can be such that some items are best put on the scrap heap.)

An early discussion of the use of heuristics, though without using the term, is by Polya (1954). His discussion, in the context of mathematics, paved the way for later work on automatic theorem-proving, especially that of Newell, Shaw and Simon (1959, 1960, also Newell and Simon 1963) on the *general problem solver*. This operates by the repeated application of a heuristic principle termed *means-ends analysis*. The principle operates in problem-solving in everyday life, and depends on examination of the difference between an existing state of the environment and a desired state. The nature of the difference is used to select an action that is likely to bring the state closer to the desired one, and the principles relating actions, or operations, to types of difference, are the principal *heuristics* involved in the method.

In the application to theorem-proving the aim is to find a sequence of operations to transform a given mathematical expression to agree with a target one, so at each application of *means-end analysis* attention is given to the difference between the target expression and the current version of the source expression. This is used to select one, or more, operations that are likely to reduce the difference, and one of these operations is applied to produce a new current expression. The process halts if the expression is brought into agreement with the target, and the sequence of operations constitutes the required proof. As in human problem-solving, however, it is not usually possible to find a complete proof without some false trails and back-tracking, and the GPS must embody heuristics for deciding whether the sequence of operations it is developing is likely to succeed. If it is not, GPS goes back to an earlier stage at which there was a choice of operations that could be applied, and proceeds differently from there. The process can be viewed as exploration of a tree structure representing possible proof developments, but with heuristics employed to avoid the 'combinatorial explosion' of complexity associated with exhaustive search.

Polya's term for what we now describe as the use of heuristics is *plausible reasoning*, or simply *guessing*, as the basis for *induction*. He comments that mathematics teaching usually emphasizes the strictly deductive, or demonstrative apect. Without denying the importance of this he points out that mathematical discovery has other, less well-defined, essential features. He acknowledges that this has been recognized by famous mathematicians (as he illustrates with quotations from Euler, Leibnitz, Kepler, Laplace, Poincaré and others) but nevertheless is often overlooked. As he puts it (vol. 1, p. vi):

"Certainly, let us learn proving, but also *let us learn guessing*."

The less well-defined aspects have always been tacitly acknowledged in mathematics teaching, since students have been encouraged to acquire skill by devising their own proofs for theorems set as examples. Polya's argument is that it is possible and potentially profitable to examine these nebulous aspects. Although mathematics is only one area in which plausible reasoning is important, Polya argues that it is an area that lends itself to study in these terms. It is also an area in which students may benefit from explicit instruction about principles underlying plausible reasoning, and in an earlier publication Polya (1957, but 1st edn. 1945) presented a collection of them. Such principles are now denoted by the convenient word *heuristics*.

That Polya sees heuristics as qualitatively different from strict deductive reasoning, and as having continuous aspects, is clear from a comment (1954 vol.1 p. 7) on the *inductive attitude*:

"It involves us in saying 'maybe' and 'perhaps' in a thousand different shades."

One reason that mathematics is a useful subject-area for the study of heuristics is because the rigour of its surface-level subject matter, i.e. its deductive aspects, is in sharp contrast to the relatively vague heuristic principles, and therefore the two can be easily distinguished. This suggestion is supported by the fact that Polya begins his discussion with reference to number theory, which is a particularly clearcut area of mathematics as far as the statement of its theorems is concerned.

In introductory discussions of AI (e.g. Andrew 1983), it is usual to discuss the idea of a *heuristic* initially in the context of *well-defined problems*. Such a problem has the property that, given something purported to be a solution, an algorithmic method can be applied to determine whether it is indeed a solution. Proving a theorem in mathematics is a problem of this sort, since the rigorous nature of mathematical deduction means that the process of checking a purported proof for validity is algorithmic. This is really another way of expressing the advantage of mathematics as an area of study, in accordance with Polya.

However, not all problems of life are well-defined; in fact, the majority do not have this convenient property. The importance of the distinction can be illustrated by another reference to the pioneering work of Newell, Shaw and Simon (1959, 1960). They considered the possibility of making their general problem solver (GPS) self-improving. They thought of doing this by building a system in two parts, termed the *performance program* and the *learning program*. These correspond to the *operative automaton* and *learning automaton* postulated by Glushkov (1966) as components of any self-organizing system.

The *performance program* was to be essentially the GPS program as implemented and demonstrated in its application to theorem-proving in formal logic and mathematics. The suggestion was that the *learning program* should also be a GPS, operating on the performance program so as to change it in ways that improve its problem-solving performance. The intention was that these two constituent sub-programs should be similar, since if the GPS is truly general it should be applicable to the task required of the *learning automaton*.

It is apparent from the discussion in Newell, Shaw and Simon (1960) that a GPS satisfying the requirement for a *learning program* must differ significantly from that constituting the *performance program*. The tasks to be performed by the two are fundamentally different, since the performance program attempts to solve well-defined problems, while those on which the learning program operates are ill-defined or open-ended. Since the task of the learning program is essentially to control evolution, its representation of the performance program must be such that the changes it dictates correspond to displacement in a continuum.

Although the use of heuristics constitutes a departure from strict 'logical' operation, the heuristics are often grafted onto an otherwise strictly logical (in sense A) environment. For example, the resolution method of theorem-proving (Robinson 1965) can be implemented without heuristics, by letting the possible resolutions and factorizations be tried systematically or randomly. The time taken to find non-trivial proofs is then usually unacceptable, and much ingenuity has been applied to the devising of heuristics to direct the search in profitable directions. (Strictly, a procedure for making systematic or random trials can be considered to be a simple *heuristic* whose effectiveness can be compared with others. At the same time, in their simplest forms these methods hardly seem to warrant such description. Some of these considerations are illustrated in a simple context in Andrew (1983).)

It is also possible to use heuristics in an environment that is not strictly 'logical' in the usual meaning (sense A) of the word. Biological motor control undoubtedly relies on heuristics and similar ones are likely to prove valuable also in robotics. The nature of these heuristics is discussed in Chapter 5, and its title, used also for the book, is intended to refer to them. Their study is obviously relevant to the future development of robots, and to the understanding of biological motor activity. However, it will be clear from the view taken here of the evolution of conceptual thinking that the study of *continuous heuristics* is expected to have, eventually, profound implications concerning the nature of intelligence as a whole.

1.9 BACKGROUND

The views expressed here have been developed over a great many years, beginning with study of machine learning in the late nineteen-fifties, extending the work of Uttley (1956, 1959). Consideration was given to the acquisition of skill in manual tasks, of which car-driving and bicycle-riding tend to be favourite illustrative examples. There was a special incentive to give attention to this aspect of learning since one object of the research was to produce industrial control devices able to learn. Principles for systems of this sort were devised (Andrew 1959, 1961), and in a parallel development Gabor (1954, also Gabor, Wilby and Woodcock 1961) developed a *learning filter* having features in common.

There was opposition to the suggestion that these schemes represented *learning* except in a trivial sense. My own proposals were criticised on this ground by Strachey (1959). Rather surprisingly, especially since the term *learning filter* was his, Gabor himself said in reply to a question from Pask (1961a) that he considered this work to have no bearing on human learning.

Andrew, and Gabor *et al*, were not the only workers to put forward schemes of essentially this kind. Another was Kalman (1958), whose ideas have been elaborated over the years and are now accepted as an important part of control theory (Sorenson 1985) with application also in statistics (Visser and Molenaar 1988). Numerous papers at the first IFAC Congress (IFAC 1961) discussed ingenious schemes for self-adjusting devices, a number of them stemming from the famous Institute of Automation and Remote Control in Moscow. It looked, in fact, as though AI and control theory were becoming quite closely interwoven. For reasons unknown, the tendency to merge did not continue in the following years, and the subject-areas of AI, control theory and cybernetics have come more and more to follow separate paths.

The above-mentioned rejections of *learning filters* as significant models of learning is consistent with already-mentioned and widely-held preconceptions about the nature of thought. However, there are reasons for thinking that the *learning filter* approach should not be lightly dismissed. One is that the acquisition of manual skill can hardly be described in any other terms, so the learning filter has to be accepted as a type of model appropriate to at least this kind of learning. However, if this is accepted it is necessary also to concede that there may be at least indirect relevance to other kinds of learning, since it is unlikely that learning in different parts of the nervous system is totally different in its nature.

Needless to say, this argument becomes more compelling if we accept the previously-mentioned view, attributed to Sherrington, that all mental activity should be regarded as a development of motor control. Also, it is rather likely that the sceptics have failed to appreciate just how readily the approach can embody features that give it a character of self-organization rather than mere parameter-adjustment. As reviewed in Chapter 2, the adjustment process can readily be adapted so as to include the means of automatic term selection. The famous learning algorithm due to Samuel (1963) and termed by him *generalization*, is essentially a matter of adjusting the coefficients of a polynomial function, and altering its selection of terms (see section 2.11), in the way suggested for learning filters. Programs for regression analysis also embody the means of altering the set of terms, either automatically or by providing data to guide the user in altering the selection manually.

It is clear that continuity plays a part in the learning of manual skills, as can be seen by considering bicycle-riding (one of the favourite illustrative situations). A person learning this skill certainly does not store disjoint packets of data on how to deal with every discriminable angle of tilt. Instead the learning is smeared over a range of tilts, allowing the amplitude of the corrective action to be appropriately related to the perceived angle.

A little reflection shows that this rather obvious remark about bicycle-riding is, in a very simple context, an example of the application of the idea of *heuristic connection* (Minsky 1963), or of the associated *basic learning heuristic* (Minsky and Selfridge 1961). Bicycle-riding can be seen as a succession of 'problems' of selecting an appropriate response to sensory inputs. Minsky and Selfridge had in mind the much more complex problem domains that have been the main concern of workers in AI. The fact that the same principle of continuity is applicable in these two widely-different contexts supports the contention that complex-symbol-based thought has evolved from simpler processes playing a part in motor control and continuous regulation.

The observation that some principles, enunciated in connection with AI, have counterparts applicable in simple continuous environments, has been dignified (Andrew 1977) by the title *Principle of Elementary Exemplification*. The exploitation of environment continuity in bicycle-riding is an *elementary exemplification* of *heuristic connection*, and it is easy to find other examples. People are remarkably ready to invoke the principles of metrical information-processing in the context of the structural or concept-based kind. This seems to be an important clue to the deep nature of thought processes.

This point of view has been argued (Andrew 1982) for a good many years, and has been supported relatively recently by the work of Churchland (1986). As she says (p. 451):

> "There is an assumption, popular among philosophers, that the brain processes that make for cognition are one sort of thing, and that the brain processes that contribute to motor control belong to an entirely different category. Accordingly, the assumption may be used to justify a disregard of research on motor control by those doing research on cognition. But if we look at matters from an evolutionary and neuro-biological point of view, the assumption is not only theoretically naive, it in fact trammels the theoretical imagination."

It is particularly interesting (and encouraging) that Churchland supports her views by discussion of a hypothetical sensory robot. This agrees with the contention here that considerations arising in robotics are likely to stimulate valuable new viewpoints.

A point of view that seems to be at the opposite end of the spectrum of possibilities is discussed by Bobrow (1984), de Kleer and Brown (1984) and other authors in the same volume. It has been found possible to represent a great deal of the theory of physics in a form that is qualitative rather than quantitative. The branches of physics to which attention has been given are those of the ordinary old-fashioned school physics; that is to say, they include Newtonian mechanics, the gas laws, and so on, but not quantum theory or relativity. The term *naive physics* is often used to denote the set of physical principles that must somehow be embodied in a living or artificial system if it is to interact in an intelligent way with a real-world environment.

The suggestion that physical laws can be usefully represented in qualitative terms is startling, since Newtonian mechanics is usually seen as inseparable from differential calculus. For many purposes, however, qualitative versions of the laws suffice. In fact, the qualitative versions tend to be used, even by persons well-acquainted with quantitative mathematical methods, in explaining or analyzing an observed effect. For example, in explaining the working of a diesel engine, it would be said that a charge of air is compressed in the cylinder and thus becomes sufficiently hot to ignite the injected fuel. It is not necessary, at least in the first instance, to refer to the thermodynamic law that would allow estimation of the temperature rise as a function of amount of compression. It is sufficient to recall the version of the law which simply says that gases become hot when they are compressed.

Of course, the qualitative version of the law does not supplant the full version for all purposes. If the principle of the diesel engine had merely been proposed but not demonstrated, people would want to be assured that the temperature rise could be sufficient to ensure combustion, before investing in a company to make such engines. The qualitative laws provide heuristics for exploring the consequences of the quantitative versions, and the sugggestion is made by de Kleer and Brown (1984) that it could be advantageous to modify physics teaching to give more attention to qualitative laws.

There is, however, a hint of circularity in their argument that an advantage of the qualitative versions is the greater ease of communicating them to a machine, and of using them thereafter. Any existing machine capable of accepting and employing such laws (in either form) must operate within the paradigms of AI. Since these have been developed on the assumption that they should operate 'logically' (in sense A) it is perhaps not surprising that they are suited to qualitative assertions. This advantage of qualitatve assertions should be qualified as being with regard to the current state of the art.

The distinction between qualitative and quantitative versions of physical laws is not the one that is at the heart of the present discussion. Newton represented physical phenomena, including the motions of the planets and falling apples, in terms of force, mass, velocity, acceleration and so on, and his *laws of motion* gave relationships between these. In doing this he was already using concept-based processing.

Apart from their formal representation due to Newton (or, for that matter, the alternative due to Einstein), some reflection of a subset of the *laws of motion* is held in the nervous systems of people and animals and used in everyday motor control. This reflection is not in any of the formalisms of physics, since it is possible to be agile and dexterous without being aware of formal methods. It is interesting to note, however, that one incentive for research with a bearing on robotics is the idea that sporting performance might be improved by bringing formal mathematical methods to bear, as by Morecki, Ekiel and Fidelus (1984).

De Kleer and Brown argue that the qualitative representation of physical principles has greater correspondence to biological control than does the traditional Newtonian one. This view receives some support from the fact that performance can often be improved by keeping in mind qualitative instructions from a teacher, even though the learner finds the instructions non-intuitive or counter-intuitive. (Beginners on the paino are told a 'correct' position for the hands, golf coaches insist on particular placings of the feet while making swings, and so on.)

Despite this, it is difficult to believe that the kind of qualitative reasoning implemented in expert systems plays a large part in anything except the 'executive' or goal-setting level of motor control. Very high levels of skill are shown by animals, both in their natural habitats and as circus performers, and it is usually accepted that their mental processes are much less symbolic than those of humans. Skilled acts depend on the informal reflection of a subset of the *laws of motion*, as mentioned above.

The important distinction, for the present argument, is that between these informal representations on the one hand, and concept-based methods on the other, irrespective of whether the latter correspond to the qualitative approach of de Kleer and Brown, or the quantitative ones of Newton and Einstein. Some further remarks about continuity in biological information processing are made in section 6.2. The contrast between the qualitative representation of physics and the traditional quantitative one is not entirely irrelevant, since the more immediate the appeal of the latter, even though it is a formal representation, probably stems from a genetic appreciation of the importance of continuity.

A class of continuous variable that has not been mentioned till now is that of estimates of *probability*, or similar estimates under the headings of *certainty*, *possibility* or *plausibility* (Klir 1988, 1989; Klir and Folger 1988). Such continuous criteria are undoubtedly involved in everyday decision-making, and not only in gambling and business environments analyzed by Luce and Raiffa (1957). Everyone knows, for example, the gradual change in the estimate of the likelihood of an accident when someone making a journey is late in arriving, from an early stage at which it would be ridiculous to phone the police to ask for information, to a later stage where it is ridiculous not to.

Numerical values related to probability, or certainty, are a feature of expert systems (Szolovits and Pauker 1984), and other areas of AI (Kanal, Levitt and Lemmer 1989). Zadeh (1983) argues for a different representation but still one requiring numerical estimates. Nevertheless, the place of probability, or certainty, estimates is controversial in *nonmonotonic reasoning* (Ginsberg 1987). The term *nonmonotonic reasoning* refers to reasoning where the available information is uncertain and possibly contradictory, in such a way that the number of possible deductions is not necessarily increased, and may be reduced, by the provision of extra input. (The number of deductions is a *nonmonotonic* function of the amount of input.)

The place of estimates of probability, or other statistics serving a similar purpose, is discussed in Chapter 2.

1.10 OVERVIEW OF THE OTHER CHAPTERS

Continuity, in the special sense discussed in section 1.4, is an important and neglected aspect of intelligence, both natural and artificial. In the remaining chapters there is further examination of its significance, with derivation of some practical implications for AI.

The connotations of continuity are numerous and varied, and it has not been easy to decide on a linear ordering for fragments of discussion that are conceptually at the nodes of a richly-interconnected semantic net. (In fact, notional representation as a net is an over-simplification since it implies a finite set of kinds of relationship between nodes.) The final order of development is, however, as follows.

In Chapter 2, relatively simple forms of continuity are treated under the title of *Evident Continuity*. This starts with a reference to Donald MacKay's early insistence (MacKay 1959) on a distinction between metrical and structural information. Since one reason for retaining metrical information is in order to form probability estimates, this leads naturally to a fuller treatment of the place of such estimates in AI. Reference is made to the connection between probability and heuristics (Polya 1954) and to a debate over the place of numerical probability estimates in nonmonotonic reasoning (Ginsberg 1987).

There is also a reference to other 'bridges' between the continuous and conceptual paradigms including *fuzzy set theory* (Zadeh 1965) and the contrast between parametric and non-parametric methods in statistics. Other 'bridges' of a different kind are provided by *catastrophe theory* (Yevin and Yablonsky 1985) and developments related to thermodynamics and *dissipative structures* (Prigogine 1971).

It is pointed out that continuity plays a part in most kinds of *pattern recognition* and that this has implications for the use of heuristics and of production rules. These in turn have implications for theories about processing in the nervous system, and for the control of industrial processes by expert systems.

The main part of the chapter is a review of principles underlying *learning filters*, and of the operation of the same or related principles in other contexts.

Modes of operation with and without an explicit model of the environment are contrasted, and also the use of odd and even objective functions. Different techniques can be used for distributing the effects of learning over a continuous phase space. It is shown that each of the two main techniques can readily be extended to have the character of self-organization rather than merely parameter-adjustment.

The intention in Chapter 3 is to show how continuity enters into types of processing that have come to be considered as essentially conceptual and discrete, and therefore the concern of traditional, or 'mainstream', AI. There is first a discussion of the assumptions implicit in some early work including that of McCulloch and Pitts (1943) and Ashby (1956). An early debate between the latter and Bellman (1964) did not receive the attention it merited.

The approach of McCulloch and Pitts is contrasted with that of Hopfield (1982) and other modern neuro-modellers who start from an assumption of continuity. The meaning to be attached to *continuity* is again discussed, with emphasis on its pragmatic character.

The idea of *heuristic connection* (Minsky 1963) is implemented, explicitly or implicitly, in programs designed to operate by *analogy* (Carbonell 1984; Chouraqui 1985; Winston 1975, 1980, 1984; Hall 1989). A continuous criteria of similarity is implicit in the study of *simulated evolution* (Fogel, Owens and Walsh 1966). The nature of the continuous criteria effective in these studies is considered. It is argued that the constitute a small subset of possible continuous criteria.

A final section of Chapter 3 discusses another kind of evidence for the effectiveness of other criteria. This is based on examination of natural language and some characteristics of jokes. The conclusion is that much that has been written about the formation and utilization of discrete concepts applies with equal force to continuous criteria.

In Chapter 4 the evolutionary viewpoint is elaborated, with the argument that the tendency to use discrete concepts has been evolved as a heuristic. There is general agreement with the work of Lenat (1984), but the treatment differs from his in that attention is focussed on evolutionary developments that may be pre-linguistic.

The ideas can be illustrated by reference to a primitive swimming organism that assists its trophic or phobic activity by making tail-flicks that produce random re-orientation. Appreciation of the set of conditions under which a tail-flick is appropriate constitutes a simple example of the use of a concept. Some computer programs for automatic optimization have essentially the same character; for example, that of Rosenbrock (1960) has a reorientation mechanism explicitly included.

The chapter ends with a discussion of evolutionary history which reveals a curious alternation of discrete and continuous processing at different stages. This emphasizes the complexity of their interaction.

In Chapter 5 the idea of a *heuristic* is extended to operation in a continuous environment. Such an extension is important in the short term for the development of robotics, and in view of what has been said about the origins of intelligence it is clear that it can have much wider significance. In this chapter the results of simulation experiments are presented.

Chapter 6 gives a summing-up of the main conclusions and their significance, with some further references to related work.

2

Evident Continuity

2.1 INTRODUCTION

The aim here is to discuss relatively direct ways in which continuity enters into intelligent behaviour and its simulation, starting with a reference to Donald MacKay's early insistence on a distinction between metrical and structural information. He discussed this with reference to computing techniques, but his interest was the achievement of a form of artificial intelligence.

The use of probability estimates is discussed, and also various 'bridges' between the continuous and conceptual paradigms. There is a review of principles underlying *learning filters*, and of a number of related schemes for achieving intelligent behaviour by continuous techniques.

2.2 ANALOG AND DIGITAL COMPUTING

At the time when digital computers came to be fairly widely available, analog computing tended to be seen as old-fashioned and unexciting. There is some justification for the ready dismissal of analog methods in the observation that anything that can be done on an analog machine can be emulated, with any desired precision, digitally.

Unfortunately, enthusiasm for digital methods was often allowed to obscure the importance of continuity. The idea that it was unimportant was encouraged by Shannon's demonstration (Shannon and Weaver 1949) that information content could be assessed in the same units for both discrete and continuous data.

In fact neither of these reasons for ignoring continuity holds up under closer inspection. Digital computers operate on binary digits and are therefore 'logical' in sense A of the previous chapter. However, most of their operations treat strings of such digits as *numbers*, and so continuity, in the wide sense in which the term is used here (see section 1.4) is built into them from the start. Shannon's result was reached by devoting sections of his paper to separate consideration of the discrete and continuous situations, and in any case there is no claim that his evaluation of information content recognizes every significant aspect of the message.

During this time, Donald MacKay was steadfast (MacKay 1959) in claiming that analog methods, and hence continuous variables, had their place in any system to warrant description as intelligent. His main arguments were in terms of practical ('operational') aspects of the necessary processing. While accepting the in-principle equivalence of the two forms of computing, he pointed out that significant features of a situation, or relationships between sets of data, could be much more easily recognized with analog representation.

The word *analog* is ambiguous. It sometimes implies that a computing process is non-digital from start to finish. On the other hand, even a wholly digital computation may in fact constitue an analog, or analogue, of a physical process, but the correspondence is not apparent unless the inputs and outputs are suitably transformed. Such transformation is now common in digital computing practice, often under the heading of *computer graphics* because the analog representation is two-dimensional.

It would be wrong to say that computer graphics originated with AI, but certainly the needs of AI prompted the development of interactive graphics. (I can remember playing 'space wars' with Marvin Minsky on a PDP 1 in a basement of M.I.T., many years ago. Marvin had a level of skill that betokened many hours of practice, and demonstrated it by firing missles to intercept mine in mid-flight. He could perform almost equally well in the 'with gravity' version of the game, in which I very soon found my space ship falling irretrievably towards the sun.) The fact that graphic input and output devices allow powerful man-machine collaboration supports MacKay's contention that analog representation (in a wide sense of the term) is important in AI.

MacKay extended his discussion to consider the kind of representation that could underlie the use of *analogy* in thinking. This comes close to the central argument of the present book, and is discussed in Chapter 3.

Estimates of probabilities, especially conditional probabilities, presumably represent one type of continuous variable playing a part in intelligence. It is difficult to imagine how everyday decision-making could operate otherwise than by forming estimates of the probabilities of different outcomes conditional on alternative courses of action.

The well-known phenomenon of the *conditioned reflex* presumably depends on estimation of the conditional probability of the *conditioned stimulus* given that a *unconditioned stimulus* has occurred. If the estimate exceeds the thresh-old level, the conditioned stimulus (ringing of a bell in the classical Pavlov experiment) produces a response (salivation in the classical study), originally associated with the unconditioned stimulus (presentation of food). Artifacts to model the conditioned reflex have been described by Walter (1953, see also Freeman 1986) and by Uttley (1956, 1959).

It was the attempt to apply Uttley's *conditional probability computer* to practical problems of control that initiated the train of thought culminating in the present volume, as related in section 1.9. Although the c.p.c. utilizes continuity in one respect, in that it forms probability estimates, its inputs and outputs are simple yes/no channels. Unless the principle is extended (Andrew 1959), the device cannot operate effectively in a continuous environment. (At least, so it seems to me. My debates with Albert Uttley on this point did not result in either being won over to the other point of view, but I found them extremely useful for clarifying my own ideas.)

The formation of estimates of probability, or something closely related, arises in at least two other important contexts discussed in the following two sectioms.

2.3 INDUCTION

In his discussion of *induction* which can be seen as introducing the idea of a *heuristic*, Polya (1954) refers to levels of strength of belief, or *credibility*. He sees a heuristic (or, to use his term, a suggestive contact with reality) as hav-ing a *weight* which determines its influence on the credibility of a hypothesis. Polya does not use the term *probability*, perhaps because its precise meaning is a matter of debate among philosophers (von Mises 1939), though physicists and statisticians manage to assign precise numerical values without first resolving the philosophical questions. Polya's *credibility* is essentially an estimate of proba-bility of truth of the hypothesis, according to the usual intuitive interpretation.

The rules determining changes in level of credibility are quite complex. Each observation that is in agreement with the hypothesis strengthens its credi-bility, and in the case of the precise hypotheses of mathematics a single contrary observation permanently reduces credibility to zero. The size of the increase in credibility, consequent on a consistent observation, depends on a variety of factors. The increment is not great if the observation is also consistent with an alternative hypothesis, especially if the latter is simpler or more general. Also, the increment is not great if the addition of the new observation does not sig-nifcantly alter the extent to which the range of possible situations is explored in the total of observations on record.

The above rules are examples of *continuous heuristics* since their effect is to modify a continuous estimate. However, their operation is less amenable to experimental examination than is that of the continuous heuristics related to motor control as discussed in Chapter 5. Rather surprisingly, the use of quantitative estimates of probability is regarded as controversial in discussions of *nonmonotonic reasoning* (Ginsberg 1987).

2.4 NONMONOTONIC REASONING

This term has been used to denote reasoning having the property that a conclusion that is accepted as true at some stage may be withdrawn when further information becomes available. The reasoning is *nonmonotonic* in the sense that extra data does not necessarily produce an increase in the number of supportable deductions. In everyday experience, many decisions have to be taken on the basis of flawed information. There are different ways in which information may be inexact. It can be just plain wrong, either because of a deliberate attempt to deceive, or because of faulty memory or judgement or a transmission error in a data link. A different kind of imprecision occurs in general statesments such as 'birds can fly' or 'canaries are yellow', the implication being that *all* birds can fly and *all* canaries are yellow.

There are, of course, categories of birds that do not fly, including ostriches and penguins, as well as birds with broken wings, feet set in concrete, etc. A deductive process, either in a brain or an artifact, is likely to deduce from the information 'x is a bird' that x can fly, but this conclusion has to be withdrawn if it is indicated that x is a penguin. The reasoning is *nonmonotonic* in the sense that the provision of an extra input does not necessarily allow an increase in the number of inferences, and may cause some to be withdrawn.

An obvious way of overcoming the difficulty is to associate a numerical estimate of *probability* or *confidence* with the general rule 'birds can fly'. However, this would not correspond to the way people commonly deal with such matters. When a reference is made to a 'bird's-eye-view', it is never the intention (unless as a joke) that this should indicate a penguin's-eye view, or even the view seen by an ordinary bird temporarily standing on the ground.

The word 'intention' is of course the key to the seeming contradiction. When a reference is made to a 'bird', the listener's interpretation is constrained by what he guesses to be the speaker's intention. The appropriate world-model for interpretation is not a zoologists's catalogue of known types of bird; it is one that might contain much less information on birds as such, but does include a representation of the speaker. Reasoning on the basis of this world-model tends to have a 'logical ' character in that it makes little if any use of probability estimates. It is in fact such that all the relevant probabilities are either trivially different from zero or trivially different from one.

McCarthy (1980) discusses nonmonotonic reasoning with reference to the well-known missionaries-and-cannibals puzzle, defined as follows:

"Three missionaries and three cannibals come to a river. A rowboat that seats two is available. If the cannibals ever outnumber the missionaries on either bank of the river, the missionaries will be eaten."

As he says, the puzzler is obviously expected to devise a strategy of rowing the boat back and forth that gets them all across and avoids the disaster. There is something strange in the readiness with which people see the problem as demanding a solution in these terms, without asking whether the boat is sound and equipped with oars, whether there is a bridge or a larger boat in the vicinity, and so on. The statement of the puzzle does not exclude either the possibility that the boat is unworkable or that there are alternative ways of getting across.

As MacCarthy acknowledges, the other possibilities would not be so readily dismissed by a person who was sitting beside a real river bank when the six people came by and posed their problem. When the problem is posed in the abstract the types of solution to be considered are constrained by assumptions about the intention of the poser. Our culture inspires respect or skill in solving self-contained 'logical' problems, so this one is forced into the mould.

Cultural values of this sort are not capricious; they have been evolved and reflect the fact that 'logical' reasoning (in sense A of the previous chapter) has practical utility. The observation about the person sitting on a real river bank shows, however, that such reasoning is not the only kind that is important. If the problem had been posed in a book advocating *lateral thinking* (de Bono 1970), the effect of the reasonable assumption about the poser's intention would be to encourage the puzzler to consider a wide range of options (bridge, larger boat, helicopter, tunnel, running jump, wading, swimming, trek round the head of the river, etc.) and to tackle the problem in the customary way only as a last resort.

McCarthy is probably right in saying that probability estimates are not useful in the kind of *nonmonotonic reasoning* that has received attention in his work and the other approaches included in Ginsberg's selection. Ginsberg says that he himself has moved towards this point of view, even though in an earlier paper (Ginsberg 1985) he outlined an approach depending on numerical probabilitites. The type of reasoning considered in this work depends on some abstraction of the properties of what may be termed the 'real' world, as in the missionaries-and-cannibals problem. (The term 'real' world is imprecise, since human interpreters like McCarthy and Ginsberg are real enough. The intention is to refer to the world as sensed directly without prior interpretation by other intelligences.)

To say that *nonmonotonic reasoning* deals with abstractions of the 'real' world is not to deny its relevance to human thought and culture. On the contrary, the most highly-regarded manifestations of intellect depend heavily on abstractions. At the same time, the brain is still, as Ashby put it, a "specialised organ of survival" and many important tasks require interaction with the 'real' world. One such task is medical diagnosis, and the use of numerical estimates of *confidence* or *likelihood* is customary in expert systems for this and similar tasks (Szolovits and Pauker 1984). The place of probability estimates in *non-monotonic reasoning* is open to debate but has little bearing on the value of such estimates in intelligent activities more closely coupled to the 'real' world.

2.5 FUZZY SET THEORY AND OTHER BRIDGES

Zadeh (1965) observed that many words in a language have imprecise meanings. To say that a man is tall does not indicate with certainty that his height exceeds some agreed threshold of tallness such as 180 centimetres, nor that a man described as not tall is necessarily shorter than this. Zadeh argued that the intuitive idea of tallness is best represented by reference to a *fuzzy set* of tall men. This is clearly a subset of the set of all men, and the term *fuzzy* indicates that the membership of the set is not precise. Any one man has a grade of membership of the set that is a value in the range of zero to one, as a function of his actual height. The grade must be close to one for individuals more than 190 cm tall and close to zero for those less than 160 cm and takes intermediate values for intermediate heights.

Fuzzy techniques have been enormously developed and it has been claimed (Zadeh 1983) that they provide the only consistent way of treating all the types of uncertainly that arise in expert system operation. The topic has become fashionable, to such an extent that the term 'fuzzy' is sometimes used to refer to methods for the treatment of uncertainty that do not in fact stem from Zadeh's initiative. A critical assessment of some of the work under the heading of *fuzziness* is made by Arbib (1977).

According to the evolutionary viewpoint developed here, the processing of continuous information should be seen as a primitive function of the brain, and its readiness to operate in terms of discrete concepts as a later development. The introduction of fuzziness amounts to a formal acknowledgement that concepts, such as that of tallness, have continuous aspects. These aspects may be regarded either as a carry-over from more primitive operation of nervous systems, or as a more recent development.

Whatever its relationship to evolutionary development, fuzzy set theory has proved useful in allowing the methods of conceptual thinking to be extended to encompass continuity (Pedrycz 1989). However, it does not extend them so as to remove the need for other ways of dealing with it. As Arbib points out, Newton's theory of gravitation would not have been formulated if he had chosen to ascribe to objects a grade of membership in the class of heavy bodies rather than a value of mass. Although, as reviewed in section 1.8, qualitative versions of physical laws can be useful for some purposes, the accuracy with which acts of skill are performed by people and animals suggests that their internal representation of the laws of motion is quantitative rather than qualitative (Newtonian rather than Zadehan).

Fuzzy set theory is one of a number of intellectual bridges between continuous and conceptual processing. It starts with concepts and shows how continuity can be added. *Catastrophe theory* goes in the other direction, since it shows how discontinuities can arise in a continuous environment. A similar bridge is offered by developments in thermodynamics due notably to Prigogine (1957, also Prigogine and Stengers 1984) which specify conditions for the spontaneous emergence of structure. These bridges allowing a transition from continuity to structure will be discussed again in Chapter 4 since they relate to evolutionary processes.

Among statisticians there is a running debate between the advocates of *parametric* and *nonparametric* techniques (Lehmann 1975). There is some correspondence to the contrast between continuous and concept-based processing. Nonparametric methods depend on the *ranking* of observations. For example, if we wanted to test the hypothesis that head size is correlated with IQ, we could list for each of six subjects, a, b, c, d, e, and f, values for head size and the result of an intelligence test. Then a parametric test of the hypothesis would be made by computing the *correlation coefficient, r*, according to the well-known formula:

$$ r = \frac{\sum_i (x_i - \overline{x})(y_i - \overline{y})}{\sqrt{\sum_i (x_i - \overline{x})^2 \sum_i (y_i - \overline{y})^2}} $$

In this, each of the summations is over the set of subjects, x_i denotes the head size of the i-th subject and y_i his IQ, and $\overline{x}$ and $\overline{y}$ are the respective means. According to the null hypothesis that there is no correlation between head size and IQ, the *expected value* of r is zero, and a very well-established body of theory allows the numerical value of r to be used to indicate whether or not the null hypothesis should be rejected. It is usual to reject the null hypothesis at the 0.05 level of significance. That is to say, the null hypothesis is rejected if the deviation of r from its expected null-hypothesis value is such that a deviation of at least this magnitude would occur with probability not greater than 0.05.

The nonparametric approach is to rank the subjects in order of increasing head size, say as $bcdaef$ and to make a similar ranking for IQ. Then statistics that approximately correspond to the correlation coefficient can be derived purely from the rankings, with no further attention to numerical values, and these can be used in deciding whether or not the null hypothesis can be rejected. Again the decision is with reference to a numerical level of significance.

Statisticians seem to be generally agreed that where there is a choice between the two approaches, parametric methods are more powerful. That is to say, for the same set of data and the same hypothesis to be tested, a parametric method is more likely to allow rejection of the unexciting null hypothesis. This is not usually taken to mean that the parametric method is less rigorous than the nonparametric alternative; it is attributable to the fact that the nonparametric method ignores much of the information in the data.

There are siutations in which there is no choice of method because numerical observations of one or more of the variables are not readily available or have no meaning. For example, statistics relating to intelligence could be obtained, even if intelligence tests had not been devised, by asking a teacher or employer to rank the subjects according to a subjective impression of 'intelligence', and using this as input to nonparametric methods of analysis. The same could be done for a whole range of nebulous qualitites such as diligence, artistic sensitivity, dress sense, cheerfulness and so on.

Even where numerical data is available there are possible reasons for preferring to use nonparametric methods. The use of a parametric method may require the arbitrary choice of a scale of measurement of some variable, where the alternatives are not simply linear transformations of each other. For example, musical pitch can be represented either as a frequency or as an interval in semitones relative to a standard note, and the two representations are logarithmically related. Similarly, sound intensity can be represented either logarithmically as decibels, or linearly in terms of power.

In the above example, the value computed for the correlation coefficient would be different according to whether 'head size' was represented by circumference, cross-sectional area, or volume. It is likely that the ambiguity would disappear when nonparametric methods were used, since it is unlikely that the ranking according to head size would be dependent on the method of representation. (It is possible that the ranking would be different when volume was the criterion, if there was a variety of head shapes in the sample population. In the other examples, where both measurements refer to the same physical quantity, and are monotonically related to each other, the choice of representation would not affect the ranking.)

Another, related, reason for preferring the nonparametric approach is that the theory underlying the parametric one depends on assumptions that are not always justified. The most troublesome of these is the assumption that variables are distributed in the particular fashion known as *normal* or *Gaussian*. The assumption has some theoretical justification, since the *central limit theorem* shows that a variable comes to be distributed in this way if it arises as the sum of a large number of independent random effects. For this reason the integral of the distribution function is also called the *error function*.

It is obvious that the assumption of mormality does not hold in strictly practical situations. For example, head size of individuals cannot really be distributed in Gaussian fashion, since this would imply a small but finite probability of heads of negative size. Quite a lot of attention has been given to the question of *robustness* of parametric tests under violation of assumptions; it is generally, but not universally, agreed that for practical purposes they are robust.

As far as the present discussion is concerned, the observation that parametric methods are more powerful than the alternative lends support to the view that continuous aspects of processing are important in intelligent systems. The process of abstraction by which an intelligent system improves the effectiveness of its own interaction with an incompletely-known environment must have much in common with the overt activities of a human statistician.

2.6 PATTERN CLASSIFICATION

An important subdivision of AI activity is termed *pattern classification* (with the word *pattern* used to denote a configuration of input data) or *pattern recognition* (with the word *pattern* now used to refer to a prototype configuration, or configuration category). Any reference to *classification* implies a criterion of similarity among objects. The criterion must be capable of assuming at least two distinct values, since objects grouped together must be more similar to one another than to objects outside their category.

For non-trivial classification tasks, the criterion allows many more than two values and is often continuous. It is hardly necessary to remark that pattern classification and scene analysis have continuous aspects; a quotation from Brady (1981) was used in section 1.7 to illustrate the need for continuity in robotics, and he had computer vision particularly in mind. Pattern-classification techniques provide another bridge, or interface, between continuous and discrete types of processing, since the patterns to be classified usually have continuous characteristics but the classification is discrete.

The difficulty of pattern-classification tasks tends to be underestimated because of the apparent ease with which people perform them. Nevertheless it is often remarked, when some rather simple model of learning is discussed, that although the model sheds some light on an aspect of brain functioning, the associated requirements for pattern classification pose much larger problems. For example, the establishment of conditioned reflexes ('classical conditioning'), and habituation, are discussed with reference to bells, whistles, and so on as stimuli. There is clearly a complex process of transduction from the pattern of incoming sound waves to classification as an example of a bell or whistle. (For these particular stimuli it is not clear whether it is more appropriate to regard the auditory system of the animal as having adapted to the stimuli, or whether the devices used to generate the sounds have been evolved so as to produce a strong effect on existing auditory systems. Probably there has been adaptation from both sides, but either way the problems are far from trivial, and in any case conditioning can be established with respect to types of stimulus less clear-cut then these.)

It can also happen that the 'logical' or knowledge-based approach to AI applications glosses over difficulties associated with transduction from and to the environment. The success of the approach in emulating human expertise in various fields has led to its application to industrial process control, for example by Elmaghraby, Jagannathan and Ralston (1985). The continuously-variable outputs from sensors installed in the process plant have to be transformed into two-valued (Boolean) inputs to the production rules of an expert system. It is, of course, interesting to see how well a process can be controlled in this way, in sharp contrast to traditional control methods. The answer has a bearing on the debate between the writer and Albert Uttley, referred to in section 2.2 above, and to the qualitative representation of physical laws discussed in section 1.8.

The initial results of Elmaghraby et al suggest that effective control is possible using the expert system approach. However, they cannot be said (and do not claim) to have ignored continuous aspects of the problem in setting up the control system.

The predicates occurring in production rules for process control can include entries of the form 'x is increasing' or 'x is high'. However, the predicate 'x is increasing' has to be understood, or shown by another rule to be, equivalent to 'the current value of x is larger than the previous one by a margin', where the margin is specified numerically. Similarly, the predicate 'x is high' has to be given a precise meaning by reference to a numerical threshold of highness. Suitable values for margins and thresholds would be found empirically, and perhaps continuously adjusted by an automatic optimization technique.

It could be said that a very simple kind of pattern classification is required to pick out the situations in which x can be said to be increasing, decreasing, high or low. The classification rules embody the numerical parameters termed *margins* and *thresholds*. The choice of suitable numerical values must be governed by some feedback, whether automatic or manual, of a criterion of utility. They clearly cannot be set, in this case, by a procedure of the *cluster analysis* type (Everitt 1974) operating purely on the input data. It is clear that considerations of continuity are not eliminated by the use of expert system techniques in process control.

Fuzzy control methods (Pedrycz 1989) allow the adaptation of expert system techniques somewhat differently, but again with attention to continuity.

2.7 SELF-OPTIMIZATION

A great many control devices have been envisaged having the property of *self-optimization*. They are able to improve their performance of a control task by adjusting one or more of their own internal parameters. The means of evaluating a numerical criterion of quality of performance is normally built-in. Selfridge (1956) coined the attractive term *hedony* for such a criterion and other workers including Andrew (1959, 1961) have continued its use. Wiener (1948), referring primarily to living systems, used the term *affective tone* for the same purpose.

As was discussed in section 1.3, there is a difficulty in defining any term referring to self-modification of an entity, and hence in defining self-optimization. The difficulty is in dividing the stored information into a part that is held to define the entity and another that is seen as data passing through it. For the remainder of this chapter the difficulty will be ignored. This is convenient and is justifiable since there is usually a fairly strong intuitive feeling about how the stored information should be partitioned. However, it should be kept in mind that the treatment is not completely rigorous.

Self-optimization, sometimes called *self-tuning*, is a means whereby the control device inproves its own performance as a result of experience, and is therefore an elementary form of *learning*. A control device usually receives input signals, say a, b and c, from transducers in the process plant or other system being controlled, and exerts control through its output signals d and e. An estimate of hedony, or degree of goal-satisfaction, must also be computed, on the basis of a, b and c and perhaps other sensory data.

The adjustable parameters could be simply static values of d and e. For example, it may be useful to adjust the temperature and pressure in a vessel so as to maximize the rate at which a chemical reaction proceeds. The rate, or productivity, of the reaction would be represented as hedony or h. In other situations the parameters may affect the control signals less directly. In the *learning filter* developed by Gabor *et al* (1961), and in similar schemes due to Andrew (1959) the adjustable parameters were of coefficients in a polynomial function. In the application of an *expert system* approach to process control, referred to in section 2.6, it was suggested that the parameters subjected to automatic optimization should include *thresholds* and *margins*. These parameters determine how indications of levels and rates of change are converted to discrete signals.

2.8 ODD AND EVEN OBJECTIVE FUNCTIONS

The quantity hedony can also be termed *objective function* to be maximized, and a vast literature (Schwefel, 1981, Andrew 1985) is devoted to methods for automatic optimization. Much of the literature is concerned with the optimization of computer models, rather than with optimization during interaction with the real-world environment, but many of the underlying principles are the same. The computer model has the advantage of reproducibility of responses, so there is less need to apply statistical principles than in the real-world situation.

It is necessarty to distinguish two very different classes of situation. When a particular set of values of the control variables is applied to the environment, or to the computer model, the resulting evaluation of the objective function may or may not be accompanied by an indication of how the control signals might have differed to produce a better result. This may be only of the sign of the difference, or may also give some idea of magnitude.

Andrew (1989) has distinguished the situations be reference to operation with and without *error-information*. Operation with error-information corresponds to the availability of an objecive function, to be minimized and having a minimal value of zero, such that its sign indicates how the control signal should be altered to bring the objective function nearer to zero. Such an objective function can be said to be an odd function of the control signal. The situation where there is no error-information corresponds to an even objective function.

Where the self-optimizing device is required to generate a binary (yes/no) signal, error-information is automatically available since if the computed value is wrong the correct answer can immediately be inferred. A *perceptron* (Rosenblatt 1959, 1961; Nilsson 1965; Minsky and Papert 1969) is usually described as having only one *response unit* and hence only a single yes/no output. It therefore automatically has error-information available to it. (It is usually discussed with only one response unit, to be trained to respond to a single pattern category. The argument is, of course, that if the principle is demonstrated for one category there is no difficulty in principle in extending it to any number.)

Even if its output were not constrained to be two-valued the perceptron is an example of a learning system operating 'with a teacher', in the sense that, during its training phase, every presentation of a sample pattern is accompanied by an indication of the correct classification. Such operation implies that error-information is available.

Rather surprisingly, the distincition between operation with and without error-information has been overlooked in two important discussions in this area. Selfridge (1959) discussed a generalization of the perceptron idea, under the title of *pandemonium*. This introduced important new principles having a bearing on self-organization (see section 2.11, below), but included a discussion of hill-climbing techniques which is inappropriate in the context because it ignores error-information. Also the applications suggested by Gabor *et al* (1961) for the *learning filter* are such that a signed indication of error is available, and yet adjustment was based purely on minimization of the squared magnitude of error. This meant that information on the sign of the error was not utilized. It is therefore hardly surprising that Lubbock (1961) was able to describe an alternative method, using error-information, that converges much more rapidly.

The optimization process may be visualized geometrically, in the manner suggested by the term *hill-climbing* (though minimization would correspond to *pothole-descending*). Error-information is then equivalent to knowledge about gradients on the response surface. In the even-objective-function situation, where information on gradients is not immediately available, it can be inferred by sampling the response at a number of adjacent points.

At least, the gradient can be inferred from simple sampling in the noise-free computer-model case (though even here there may be problems about choosing suitable increments between sampling values). In the real-world noisy situation repeated sampling may be needed to obtain a reliable indication, and it may be more convenient to think of the process in terms of the imposition of experimental fluctuations on the parameter-values, and the evaluation of the correlation between these fluctuations and the indication of objective function or hedony. The process has been analyzed by Andrew (1967a, 1989a) in the case where the adjustable parameters are coefficients in a polynomial function.

Suppose a controller operates according to the polynomial:

$$d = K + La + Mb + Nc + Pab \tag{1}$$

in which $d(t)$ is the action applied to the controlled process, and $a(t), b(t)$ and $c(t)$ are signals from sensors in it. The parameters to be adjusted are $K, L, \ldots, P$.

It is possible to superimpose fluctuations $K_f(t), L_f(t)$, etc. on the parameters:

$$d = K + K_f + (L + L_f)a + (M + M_f)b + \ldots \tag{2}$$

and then to evaluate correlations between each of the fluctuations and $h(t)$. If the aim is to maximize h, then a significant positive correlation with one of the fluctuations indicates that the associated parameter should be increased, and conversely for a significant negative correlation.

The addition of separate fluctuations to all the parameters has the disadvantage that the magnitude of the overall effect on the control signal $d(t)$ is not directly controllable. An alternative is to add one fluctuation $d_f(t)$ to d:

$$d = d_f + K + La + Mb + Nc + Pab \tag{3}$$

It is then possible to compute, at any instant, the fluctuation which, added to any coefficient, would have produced the same effect as d_f. Let K_{ef}, L_{ef}, etc. be fluctuations in K, L, etc. that would be equivalent to d_f. Then

$$K_{ef} = d_f, \quad L_{ef} = d_f/a, \quad M_{ef} = d_f/b, \quad \text{and so on.} \tag{4}$$

These equivalent fluctuations must be clipped in amplitude, since they become infinite when a, b, etc. are zero. The clipped signals can then be correlated with $h(t)$ and used to determine changes in the parameters K, L, etc. To make the clipping symmetrical, the variables a, b, etc. must be shifted to have zero means.

This seems a plausible way of computing the effective fluctuations as the basis of an optimization process. However, it has not proved satisfactory when tested by computer simulation. This is not altogether surprising in view of the fact that an equivalent fluctuation (other than the 'constant term' one, k_{ef}) takes its numerically greatest values when the associated variable (a, b, etc.) is close to its mean value. Hence, the integration providing the estimate of correlation receives its greatest contributions when the deviation of the variable from its mean value is small. The correlation is therefore an unsuitable criterion for determining the changes in the influence of this variable in the control action.

It has been found by experiment that optimization proceeds more favourably if the effective fluctuations are computed as products rather than as quotients, so that Eqn. (4) is replaced by:

$$K_{ef} = d_f, \quad L_{ef} = d_f \cdot a, \quad M_{ef} = d_f \cdot b, \quad \text{and so on.} \tag{5}$$

This form of operation has a sound theoretical justification as well as the experimental one, as will be seen in the next section.

2.9 INTERNAL MODELS

There are two main ways of visualizing a self-optimizing controller. The discussion in the last section was of a controller operating to adjust or tune its own policy of interaction with the environment, represented by Eqn. (1). An alternative is to construct and refine a model of the relevant part of the environment, and then to use the model in deriving optimal control actions.

For the control problem considered, the model could have the form of a polynomial or other function allowing the prediction of h as a function of a, b, c and d. Once the polynomial has been formed, the value of d to maximize h, for given values of a, b and c, can be derived from the well-known 'method of the calculus', i.e. by equating the appropriate derivative to zero and solving for d. The self-optimizing feature of the controller then lies in the adjustment of the model. Since this is a matter of modelling, error-information is available. The adjustment now operates in the odd-objective-function situation.

It has been shown (Andrew 1967a, 1989a) that the operation of a controller operating directly on its own control policy, as first considered, may be functionally identical to that of a controller operating by refining and referring to a model. This illustrates the difficulty, previously discussed in section 1.5, of defining what is meant by an internal model of the environment. As was observed there, any system that has evolved so as to achieve some goal in a particular environment must somehow mirror, in its evolved state, the significant features of the environment. It is a matter of subjective judgement whether this mirroring is appropriately described as a 'model'.

For adjusting a polynomial model the well-established method of *regression analysis* (Draper and Smith 1966) is available. This normally involves the inversion of a matrix, and it seems a little unlikely that biological processing follows the method exactly. If it can be assumed that the independent variables (a, b, c and d in the above example) are uncorrelated, the matrix has zero entries except on its main diagonal and the method can be reformulated so as to eliminate the need for matrix operations and to let the variables be adjusted independently of one another.

The adjustment method used by Lubbock (1961) is essentially this simplified version of regression, applied after a preliminary transformation of the inputs to ensure that they are mutually uncorrelated, or orthogonal. For this he uses the Gram-Schmidt orthogonalization method, which is also a feature of the optimization method of Rosenbrock (1960), and is described in Appendix B.

Even without prior orthogonalization the simplified method can be used as the basis of a process of successive adjustment, by letting the parameter adjustments at each step be as indicated by the method but reduced in size. If the adjustment is too large and the variables are strongly correlated, instability can result. The true regression method allows 'one shot' adjustment, and so does Lubbock's variation. The simpler method which does not evaluate correlations between the independent variables can converge on the same result by successive approximation. Because of its conceptual simplicity the successive-apporoximation method seems more plausible than the others as a model of biological learning. It is also likely to be more robust than true regression if the system to be modelled, or its environment, is not constant.

2.9.1 Error Decorrelation

The successive-adjustment method can also be formulated rather differently and corresponds to *error decorrelation* as described by Donaldson (1960, 1964). He demonstrated its effectiveness in a self-adjusting controller for a pole-balancing task (Andrew 1967b). Like a *perceptron training algorithm* (see below), it indicates directions for parameter-adjustments but does not indicate how large the adjustments should be.

The method is applied to a polynomial expression like that of Eqn. (1), and for simplicity the product term is omitted here:

$$d = K + La + Mb + Nc \tag{6}$$

The value computed as d might be an estimate or a prediction of a value whose 'correct' value becomes available for comparison, or in some other way an indication is obtained of at least the sign of the 'error' in d.

If the mean value of the error is positive, the error can be reduced by reducing the value of K, and conversely K should be increased if the mean value is negative. The mean value of error is the average product (unnormalized correlation) betweem the error and the notional input signal having constant value unity that can be considered to be multiplied by K in the first term of the polynomial.

The other parameters can be adjusted similarly by evaluating correlations between the error and the respective independent variables a, b and c. If there is positive correlation with a, the error can be reduced by reducing the value of L, and if there is negative correlation the value of L should be increased. Correlations with the other inedependent variables b and c similarly determine changes in M and N.

2.9.2 Samuel's Learning Algorithm

Samuel (1963) developed a famous program to play the game of checkers (draughts) and to improve its own performance by a learning process. It embodied two kinds of learning, which he termed *rote-learning* and *generalization*. The latter is the more interesting , and constitutes a means of adjusting the coefficients of the *evaluation function* or *scoring polynomial* used to make the static evaluation of board configurations represented at terminal nodes of the lookahead tree. (The evaluation is 'static' in the sense of not depending on further lookahead.)

Although it has a number of *ad hoc* embellishments which Samuel found to be advantageous, this famous learning algorithm is essentially a matter of *error decorrelation*. The result of evaluating the polynomial cannot be compared with any 'correct' or 'ideal' value in order to determine an 'error' However, it can be compared with a value that is arguably preferable to that obtained by direct evaluation of the polynomial, namely a value obtained by the now well-known technique of minimax back-up through a lookahead tree. Provided certain precautions are taken to ensure that the evaluation has some bearing on quality of play, this backed-up evaluation is arguably closer than the static one to an ideal value that would result from exhaustive lookahead.

2.9.3 Perceptrons

The *perceptron* principle (Rosenblatt 1959) received much attention in the nineteen-fiftes and early sixties. Minsky and Papert (1969) estimated that, in the heyday of enthusiamsm for the idea, at least a hundred research groups were working on versions of it. The principle, at least in the restricted version termed a *simple perceptron*, is well-known and is described in a number of popular texts, for example Andrew (1983). It is very briefly recapitulated below.

A *simple perceptron* is a trainable, pattern-classifier made up of three layers of threshold elements that can be termed model neurons. The first layer consists of *sensory units* (or *s*-units) which could be the light-sensitive cells of a retina, and the pattern to be classified is imposed on this. Units in this layer are randomly connected to those in the next layer of *association units* or *a*-units, so that each *a*-unit is responsive to a particular randomly-formed feature of the imposed pattern.

The final layer consists of *response-units* (or *r*-units), each corresponding to a pattern class. Each *r*-unit receives inputs from all the *a*-units, the signal in each input being two-valued since the *a*-units are threshold devices. The *r*-unit sums contributions from the subset of its inputs coming from *a*-units that have 'fired'. The contribution of a particular input, or *synapse*, is equal to a quantity termed its *weight*. The device can be trained to perform a particular classification task by presenting a succession of sample patterns, along with an indication of the correct classification. The effect of the training is to modify the synaptic *weights*, and a rule for making the modification is called a *training algorithm*.

Minsky and Papert damped enthusiasm for perceptrons, mainly by demonstrating limitations on what could be achieved by a *simple perceptron*. Of course, the restriction to the *simple perceptron* meant that the arguments were inconclusive for perceptrons in a wider sense, but, as these authors pointed out, the wider sense was ill-defined and could include virtually any pattern-classifier embodying neuron-like elements.

Despite the limitations, exploration of the perceptron idea served a useful purpose, as acknowledged by Malsburg (1986). It crystallized something definite and testable out of a mass of rather diffuse speculation. It produced a variety of perceptron training algorithms, shown by Nilsson (1965) to be similar except in the precise rules used to determine the magnitude of the adjustment of synaptic weights. The rules received a great deal of attention from mathematicians, and it has been remarked that the *perceptron convergence theorem* has a claim to being the most proved theorem in mathematics, because of the variety of distinct proofs advanced. Two that are particularly succinct are presented by Nilsson.

The *training algorithm* can be seen as another example of *error decorrelation*. It does not involve the computation of correlations as such, because the adjustable parameters (the weights of the synaptic connections to the response unit) are adjusted following each trial in which the classification is incorrect. This means that instead of using separate integrators to evaluate correlations, the parameters themselves are the integrators. The error indication following each trial during the training period can take one of three values, being zero if the classification was correct, +1 if the pattern was accepted as belonging to the category (i.e. the *r*-unit fired) when it should not, and -1 if the error was the other way round.

For each synaptic connection from an *a*-unit which was active, the weight is modified by an amount depending on the error indication, usually simply proportional to it. This means that the modification is determined by the product of the state of excitation, expressed as zero or one, and the indication of error. The value obtained by integrating or smoothing such a product is proportional to the correlation between the excitation and error. The summation performed by the *r*-unit can be expressed as a polynomial function in which the states of excitation of the synapses are independent variables and the synaptic weights are the coefficients to be adjusted. Viewed in this way, the training algorithm can be seen to be an example of error decorrelation.

2.10 LEARNING FILTERS

The term *learning filter* was coined by Gabor (1954, also Gabor, Wilby and Woodcock 1961) to refer to a device continuously evaluating a polynomial function of a set of inputs, and adjusting the function so as to improve its own performance, according to some agreed criterion. The adjustment of the function is mainly by parameter-adjustment, but a mechanism is also provided for modifying the selection of terms. This is discussed in the next section. A similar scheme was devised independently by Andrew (1959, 1961).

As recalled in section 1.9, a great deal of consideration was given to systems of this general sort in the nineteen-fifties and early sixties, and a particular formulation termed *Kalman filtering* has found favour in control engineering. Since the polynomial can have terms of degree higher than unity in the independent variables, the filter function can be non-linear. One of Gabor's motivations in considering such filters was the possibility they offered of extending practical control methods to include non-linear functions. Existing theory, largely due to Wiener, was adequate for the analysis and synthesis of linear systems, but there was (and is) no corresponding comprehensive treatment of the enormously greater variety of non-linear systems.

The term *filter*, as used in electronics, or in other practical contexts such as water or air purification, usually implies a device having a single input and a single output. Also, in electronics it implies a device having a certain amount of memory, so that the output at any instant is not only a function of the input at the same instant, but is also influenced by its value at earlier instants. In fact, a linear filter can be completely specified by giving its *response function*, or output pattern in time following an input impulse.

The inputs, or independent variables, appearing in the polynomial function of a *learning filter* can include time-displaced values. Any linear filter, in the sense intended in the context of electronics, can be approximated as a linear sum as follows:

$$d = K_1 s(t) + K_2 s(t - \tau) + K_3 s(t - 2\tau) + \dots \tag{7}$$

where $s(t)$ is the input to the filter and d its output and τ is a small increment in time. The summation must be continued up to a term in which the time-displacement represented as a multiple of τ is long compared to all *time-constants*, or inherent memory durations, in the filter. The reason for Gabor's interest in this form of representation is that extra terms can readily be added to produce a non-linear filter, which can then be automatically adjusted, by the methods described, so as to satisfy some requirement.

2.11 SELF-ORGANIZATION

One reason that systems of the *learning filter* type have been thought to be uninteresting from the AI point of view is that their *learning* seems to be within a restricted range of possibilities. The form of polynomial remains the same, irrespective of changes in parameter values. At least, mechanisms discussed in this chapter up to now have only allowed for parameter adjustment, but they are readily extended to allow the automatic selection of polynomial terms and hence changes in the form of the polynomial.

The possibility of changes in form implies a property of *self-organization* (Andrew 1989), though, perhaps not surprisingly, there are difficulties of definition of this term. Apart from the difficulties associated with any term denoting self-modification, there is a difficulty in distinguishing a change in form (a qualitative change) from a mere change in a parameter value (a quantitative change). At first sight the difference seems clear enough, but functionally there is no difference between the insertion of a new term into the polynomial and the shift to a non-zero value of a coefficient that had previously been zero. In some of the literature the requirement has been indicated by saying that a self-organizing system must "change its basic structure" autonomously, but this does not entirely remove the ambiguity.

In practice, there is usually a fairly definite intuitive feeling as to whether a given process is best seen as *self-organizing* or merely *self-optimizing*. In terms of electronic circuits, a system is to be seen as self-organizing if it can modify its own pattern of connections, but not if it only acts to change settings of gain. If the number of connections that could, in principle, be made, is very much greater than the number existing at any time, then the term *self-organizing* is probably warranted. A similar criterion applies to systems allowing the selection of polynomial terms.

A facility for introducing and eliminating terms is, or can be, a feature of almost all polynomial-adjusting systems considered in the foregoing. Statistics packages for regression analysis give the user help in choosing new terms that might profitably be introduced, and certainly they indicate which of the existing terms could be eliminated without much detriment. Indications for possible new terms are usually derived from examination of *residual errors*, or discrepancies between the result of evaluating the regression polynomial and the true values it is intended to model. The problem received early attention in the AI literature with the description of a method (Collins 1967) which, surprisingly, operates without attention to residuals, except in using them to evaluate a criterion of overall goodness of fit.

Samuel's discussion of his checker-playing program (Samuel 1963) pays a great deal of attention to the means of selecting terms to appear in the *scoring polynomial* or *evaluation function*. In the program as used in the runs reported, 38 possible 'simple' terms were defined (in addition to the *piece-advantage* term which was always included to ensure that the function did not collapse into one having no bearing on effective play). Of these 38 possible terms, 16 were included in the polynomial at any one time and 22 were held in reserve. The means of computing each of the 38 terms was devised with the intention of embodying some principle known to be used by human expert players. Apart from the simple terms a few more complex ones were introduced, formed by combining pairs of simple terms. The set of terms effective in the polynomial was continually revised during play.

A *perceptron*, as generally understood, has a fixed set of inputs to each response unit. These come from the set of association units, each of which receives a randomly-chosen set of inputs from sensory units. The connections are made randomly when the perceptron is first constructed, but thereafter they are fixed, like the entries in a printed table of random numbers. Obviously, the rather strange 'features' that trigger association units bear no relation, unless by accident, to any structure inherent in the classification task. For example, if the task is to recognize upper-case letters of the alphabet, certain features such as a top horizontal bar as in E, F or T, are clearly significant because of the structure of the task (Selfridge and Neisser 1963). (For sloppy hand-printed characters the bar need not be straight nor continuous nor accurately horizontal but even then it is possible to find features that could be recognized by suitably connected association units, such that the firing/non-firing of the unit usually corresponds to presence/absence of a top bar.)

An obvious extension of the perceptron principle is to allow the automatic selection of 'features' computed by association units. Such an extension has been described by Roberts (1960). The connections to these units are formed randomly in the first instance. After the device has been in operation for some time it is a simple matter to determine, from the weights, the extent to which different units have contributed to the recognition process. An indication of the *worth* of an association unit can be formed as, say, the sum of magnitudes of weights of all the synapses through which it influences response units, or the sum of squares of such magnitudes, etc.

The set of 'features' computed by the association units can then be revised, by disbanding the input connections of any unit proving to have low worth. A new set of input connections can then be chosen randomly for this unit. By successsive refinement in this way, the match between the computed 'features' and the recognition task can be improved.

2.11.1 Pandemonium

These ideas were explored very fully by Selfridge (1959, also Selfridge and Neisser 1963). The term *worth* is due to him, and his *pandemonium* scheme represents a very general approach to self-organizing pattern classification. Instead of the association units of a perceptron he postulates *computational demons* (using the word *demon* to indicate a small active entity like a *Maxwell demon* in thermodynamics). These are not necessarily restricted to single threshold elements as are association units. As in Robert's version of the perceptron, demons proving to have low worth are disbanded, and new ones are formed to take their place.

Instead of letting new computational demons be formed randomly, however, Selfridge considered ways in which the choice could be guided heuristically. The idea was that the new demons should have something in common with existing ones that had proved to have high worth. One relatively straightforward way of doing this is to combine the outputs of two high-worth demons, by one of a number of 'logical' operations, and to threat the combined output as coming from a new demon. Selfridge terms this process *conjugation*.

Selfridge also tried to provide a way of forming new demons that would be more adventurous than conjugation in exploring new possibilities, and yet would be guided by what had already been recognized as of high worth. He termed the process *mutated fission* to indicate its correspondence to biological evolution. He did not find a wholly satisfactory way of implementing this, and the difficulty is common to all evolutionary processes, as discussed in Chapter 4.

2.11.2 Janet

A self-organizing system termed *Janet* (Foulkes 1959) is particularly interesting because if can 'grow' a large amount of structure to match its task environment. It receives as input a sequence of digits (or other symbols from a fixed repertoire), and for simplicity these were restricted to binary digits in the implementation described. The input sequence may have some statistical structure, and the aim of the *Janet* is to discover this and so to become able to predict the next symbol with a better-than-chance success rate. (The name *Janet* has no mnemonic significance here; it is the name of Foulkes' daughter.)

A *Janet* starts with a single unit containing four counters. These maintain totals of, respectively, the numbers of occurrences of the sequences 00, 01, 10 and 11. If the first two of these totals come to be significantly different from one another, it is possible to make a better-than-chance prediction of the digit to follow a 0-digit. Similarly, if the second two totals differ significantly, it is possible to make a better-than-chance prediction of the digit to follow a 1-digit.

Let us suppose that the former of these conditions holds and there are grounds for predicting the successor of a 0-digit. The device begins to make predictions on this basis, but also sprouts a new unit which maintains counts of the occurrences of 000, 001, 100 and 101. If the first two of these come to differ significantly from one another there are grounds for predicting the next digit to follow the sequence 00, and a new unit would be sprouted to maintain and examine counts of occurrences of 0000, 0001, 1000 and 1001, and so on.

A *Janet* can be represented, somewhat tediously, as making a prediction of the next digit by evaluating a polynomial. The independent variables are the already-received digits, starting with the most recent , then the next-most-recent, and so on. The rule for selecting new 'candidate' terms for inclusion is simply that if the digit n places back has proved useful in the prediction it may be worth considering in the same context the digit $n + 1$ places back.

It is easy to think of types of statistical structure that could be exploited for prediction but would not be unravelled by a *Janet*. More powerful approaches to the prediction problem as such are given by Witten (1978, 1979) and Gerardy (1989). However, a *Janet* is interesting as a system of the general polynomial-adjusting kind in which self-organization is an obvious and fundamental characteristic.

2.11.3 Significance Feedback

The evaluation of the *worth* of a computational demon is a feedback to it of the significance, or usefulness, of the information it provides. Such feedback could continue back through a network. For example, the new demon produced by conjugation, as discussed in section 2.11.1, would have a value of worth fed back to it. However, if this demon is of high worth, then so are the two from which it receives its inputs, even if they do not receive feedbacks of high worth from anywhere else. To produce the desirable effect of preserving these demons, the new demon formed by conjugation should feed back worth to its 'parents', and obviously they might pass it on further to elements of the network from which they obtain information.

This kind of *significance feedback* could operate throughout a net and would presumably be a useful aid to goal-directed self-organization. The idea was put forward by Andrew (1965, 1973, 1989a), without, at first, the realization that it was implicit in the *pandemonium* principle. (Although it was implicit, it was not stressed in Selfridge's presentation.). Without some means of carrying *significance* back into the net, all schemes for automatic improvement are limited to adjustments at a single functional layer. That is to say, no adjustable element of the net affects the output by acting through another adjustable element. The *simple perceptron* is clearly limited in this way and its problem-solving capability is correspondingly weak.

Significance feedback can be seen as at least a partial answer to what Minsky (1963) termed the *credit assignment problem*. In fact, for complex networks, undergoing adjustment in a goal-directed way, the significant question is not whether such feedback exists, since it certainly does in some form, but how it comes about. The suggestion that there may be pathways specifically implementing it in real nervous systems is compatible with neurophysiological data, since there are numerous fine nerve fibres to which no other function has been ascribed (Wall, Fitzgerald and Woolf 1982). Speculation about something of the sort is certainly implicit in much discussion under the heading of *parallel distributed processing* (Rumelhart, McClelland *et al* 1986).

The form of significance feedback represented in the pandemonium is only one of the possibilities. It has been termed *scalar* significance feedback, and the feedback signals need vary only slowly compared to those in the primary, forward-going paths. (The feedback is most easily visualized in networks without loops, so that the primary flow of information goes one way, and the feedback the other.). It is useful in preserving useful pathways through the net.

The feedback of this scalar criterion of utility gives no indication of how the forward-going signal might have differed in order to produce a more favourable result. In this respect it corresponds to the provision throughout the net of a value for an *even objective function* as discussed in section 2.8. It is also possible to consider *vector* significance feedback in which the feedback signals can take either sign, and may be multi-valued if the network produces several distinct outputs, or if its output is evaluated in several different ways. Such feedback could correspond to the provision of an *odd* objective function at points throughout the net.

To be useful in determining adaptive changes throughout the net, the feedack should indicate, throughout the net, how the signal value at the point of indication could have differed in order to improve the final output. The feedback must effectively perform a continuous *sensitivity analysis*, and the feedback indication is the final *error* multiplied by the sensitivity of the output to changes at the point of indication.

There are two slightly different possibilities here. One is that the feedback literally performs a continuous sensitivity analysis, and then throughout the net the error is multiplied by the sensitivity indication. The other is that the feedback of the error itself is suitably modified as it percolates back through the net. The feedback pathways are in the form of a tree growing back from the point of output of the primary net, at which the error is evaluated. The initial sensitivity of the 'trunk' of the tree must be unity, so it carries either a signal of unity (for the former possibility), or a signal representing the error (for the second).

All of the network elements that transform the primary signals must also transform the feedback signals in a corresponding way. For *vector significance feedback*, this would operate as follows for a network element that multiplied two signals in the primary paths. Suppose the input signals to the element are $a(t)$ and $b(t)$, so that the output $c(t)$ is the product of these.

$$c = a \cdot b \tag{8}$$

If the feedback signal associated with the pathway conveying c is $s(t)$, the element should transform this so as to produce a signal equal to $b \cdot s$ to be associated with the pathway conveying a, and one equal to $a \cdot s$ to be associated with the pathway conveying b. The justification for these transformations is easily seen, in terms of sensitivity, and similar transformations are easily derived for other continuous computing elements, provided their response is linear or quasi-linear.

The values made available by *vector significance feedback*, throughout the net, can be used to determine parameter changes in the same way as the *error* or *odd objective function* evaluation was used in *error decorrelation* in a single-layer situation. The method has been found to converge as expcted when applied to a small net of linear elements and some quasi-linear ones, (namely, a square-law element and a multiplier.)

Despite a good deal of experimentation, no really satisfactory way has been found of using this type of feedback to produce useful self-adjustment in networks of model neurons. The idea of 'sensitivity', as understood in a differential calculus sense, does not apply to such strongly non-linear elements. Attempts have been made to employ criteria having some apparent similarity, depending on the nearness of the current summation in the neuron to the threshold level, but simulated networks embodying the methods showed little if any tendency to produce favourable self-modification.

The method does not provide an immediate answer to the classical problem of achieving goal-directed self-organization in networks of McCulloch-Pitts model neurons. Although this is a classical problem, reasons will be given in Chapter 3 for believing it may not be as significant has has been widely believed. It may be more relevant to brain functioning to consider the self-organization of nets of quasi-linear elements than of nets of threshold elements.

Significance feedback is then a potentially useful technique. In a recent paper, Hinton (1989) uses the term *backpropogation*, apparently synonymously with *vector significance feedback*, and refers to a number of independent studies in which the idea has emerged.

2.11.4 Selection Strategies

So far, the discussion of self-organization has been mainly with reference to the odd-objective-function situations characteristic of modelling or prediction. Indications for the incorporation of new terms may arise from discovering variables that correlate significantly with the *residuals* or errors of modelling or prediction. They may also be suggested heuristically by the terms already incorporated; this is done in a simple way in Foulkes' *Janet* and is the intention in Collin's scheme for selection of regression terms (Collins 1967) and of Selfridge's *mutated fission*.

A method that is perhaps more obvious that that of testing correlations with residuals is simply to insert the term on a trial basis and to see whether the automatic adjustment process lets it retain a non-zero coefficient. This is the method of term selection in Samuel's *generalization* learning algorithm (Samuel 1963) and in Roberts' improved *perceptron*. Since the automatic adjustment depends on correlations, the method of trial insertion may be mathematically equivalent to the evaluation of correlation with residuals, but the latter is likely to be more convenient in searching for useful new terms, especially since it can utilize rather rough-and-ready estimates of correlation.

When regression is carried out manually, a new term may be suggested by a relatively crude method for detecting correlation, such as visual inspection of a scatter diagram. It is likely that self-organizing systems, including living ones, could similarly employ some sort of 'wandering correlators' to search for useful terms to be incorporated.

For operation with an even objective function, the method of trial insertion of a new term is clearly equally applicable. However, 'wandering correlators' can be used here also. If optimization is carried out by the method described in section 2.8, effective fluctuations like those of Eqn. (5) can be ascribed to any variable, whether or not it is included in the polynomial. If, for a variable not currently inluded, the effective fluctuations are found to be correlated with hedony, the variable can profitably be introduced.

2.11.5 Alternative Formulations

The discussion has been focussed very strongly on devices embodying and adjusting a polynomial function. Other mathematical functions could have been used, but the polynomial is convenient, and has already received much attention under the heading of *regression analysis*. It also has some correspondence to the addition of synaptic contributions in a model neuron. Much of the discussion here would apply equally well to other types of continuous mathematical relationship.

However, the aim is to obtain some result in a continuous environment, in a way that takes advantage of continuity (so that, for example, interpolation can be used as it is in bicycle-riding), and preferably allows self-improvement. The use of a continuous mathematical function with adjustable parameters is only one way of achieving the result.

An alternative is to let the signals from the environment $(a, b, c, \ldots)$ define a phase-space, and to let values of the outputs (corresponding to d in the previous treatment, but usually multi-valued) be stored to refer to 'key points' distributed through this space (Andrew 1959, 1967b, 1989). The phase space is probably of high dimensionality. In a non-trivial environment it is impossible to have so many key points that one is assigned to every discriminable situation that can be defined by the inputs. Even if the necessary information storage could be provided, such representation would be unsatisfactory since it would not allow the exploitation of continuity to speed-up learning of continuous tasks such as bicycle-riding.

With key points more widely spaces, we may suppose that the input values define a point P, which in general does not coincide with a key point. It is then necessary to use an interpolation procedure such that the control action (value of d, etc.) appropriate to P is determined mainly by the values stored at the key points nearest to P.

If the system is to be self-optimizing, the control action must evoke some indication of how it should have differed to produce a better result. In the odd-objective-function situation such an indication is immediately available, but with an even objective function it has to be derived by imposition of fluctuations and correlation of these with the hedony indication. In either case the interpolation procedure has to be made to work in reverse, so that the indication for change can be distributed back to the key points that determined the control action.

A suitable interpolation procedure is that described by Paynter (1960) and Philbrick (1960) using hyper-polyhedric functions. This procedure does not depend on regular spacing of the key points.

The method is limited by the fact that the control action must change monotonically and smoothly as the operating point moves through a region of the phase-space not containing a key point. This restriction becomes less severe as the density of key points increases, eventually becoming non-existent when there is a key point corresponding to every discriminable combination of inputs. At this stage, as noted above, the system ceases to exploit continuity.

The key point method can be rendered more flexible by a process of self-organization corresponding to that used to alter the form of polynomials. The system can have the means of detecting that interpolation is unsatisfactory when the operating point falls in a particular region of the phase-space. This would indicate that extra key points should be added in this region. A means of eliminating unnecessary points can also be introduced.

The criterion for deciding that interpolation is unsatisfactory in a region could depend on detection of inconsistency in the indications for alteration of the stored values associated with the key points. If the variations in the indications are found to be correlated with the operating-point location, in an interval between key points, the interval is too large, and a new key point can profitably be interposed.

The criterion for removing a key point would be simply that it should be eliminated if the control action determined by its stored information is close to that which would in any case have been obtained by interpolation from other points.

It is interesting that the key-point method lends itself to self-organization in essentially the same way as does the polynomial method. The key point method has some intuitive appeal as a model of human performance in a continuous environment. However, it does not readily allow the incorporation of completely new variables, since each of these requires a further dimension to be added to the phase-space, increasing its dimensionality from, say, n to $n+1$. The information that was stored for each key point in n dimensions must then be copied to at least two points in the $n + 1$ dimensional space, these points being separated in the newly-added dimension.

This duplication of information is clumsy compared to the simple introduction of a new variable in a polynomial or other continuous function. The polynomial method seems much more plausible as a model of how a bicycle-rider adjusts his internal representation in order to take account of a new variable such as the strength of a side-wind (assuming that his previous experience was without this complication). On the other hand, the key-point method may have greater relevance where the new variable is only significant within a small part of the phase-space defined by the other variables. It is likely that the brain demonstrates its versatility by employing some combination of the two methods.

The key point method introduces interpolation at the time of making an action, whereas the polynomial method has continuity, and hence the possibility of interpolation, implicit from the start. Given that continuity is a feature of the environment, the polynomial method has more of the character of neural processing as discussed by Anderson and Hinton (1981, see also Andrew 1987b). These authors argue that neural processing differs from electronic computation in that the representations are less abstract, having internal structure that is in some sense an image of something in the real world.

2.11.6 Self-organization and Evolution

A central argument of this book is that processes underlying *intelligence* have evolved from more primitive ones concerned with continuous control, and that important aspects of intelligence can only be understood in the context of this evolutionary development. An important step in such evolution would be the appearance of self-organization as a feature of a system performing continuous control. The various possiblities reviewed here, for mechanisms of self-organization, are therefore interesting from an evolutionary point of view. Other aspects having a bearing on this are discussed in the remaining chapters.

2.12 DAISYWORLD

Although evolutionary aspects are to be treated in Chapter 4, it is worth while looking at a mechanism by which a regulatory effect can emerge from a system which has none of the expected characteristics of a control mechanism. The model was suggested by Lovelock (1983, 1986, also Watson and Lovelock 1983) in connection with *global homeostasis*, or the regulation of such environmental variables as the surface temperature of the earth, oxygen content of the atmosphere, and salinity of the ocean. The explanation is elegant and compelling in the global context, and it would be surprising if internal regulation in living systems did not have its origins in something similar. Some further discussion and development of the idea is given by Andrew (1988b).

Lovelock (1979) has advanced a "new look at life on Earth", conveniently referred to as the *Gaia hypothesis*, the name Gaia being one given to the Greek earth goddess. In this, he rejects the common assumption that environmental conditions on the earth just happen to be compatible with life. He suggests, instead, that these conditions are best seen as being regulated at levels conducive to the existence of living systems. The regulation is imposed by the totality of living organisms in the biosphere, constituting one giant animal with internal homeostasis, and poetically identifiable with the earth goddess.

It is not difficult to show that the environment is much influenced by biological activity; without it, for instance, there would be very little atmosphere since in thermodynamic equilibrium the bulk of both the oxygen and the nitrogen would be locked up in non-gaseous forms. Given that there is such a powerful influence, it is perhaps not outrageous to suggest that the effect might be to impose regulation. Lovelock suggests various channels through which biological activity might control environmental variables.

The *Gaia hypothesis* does not contradict the Darwinian view of evolution, but somewhat modifies it. Living species evolve so as to be compatible with the global environment, but it is wrong to assume that the environment remains constant, or is only affected by non-biological influences. The hypothesis is that an aspect of the evolutionary development is the finding of ways of regulating the global environment. It is easy to think of evolutionary developments that regulate a very local environment, as do fur and feathers as well as nests, burrows and so on, but the suggestion that the global environment is regulated is more startling. Lovelock is able to point to the fact that global variables, particularly the surface temperature of the earth, have remained remarkably steady over a period in which the sun's power has presumably increased by 25% (on the assumption that the sun is behaving like other stars).

It is sometimes claimed that man is 'master of his environment', and certainly modern technology has advanced the nest-building type of activity to the stage where comfortable nests are regularly speeding through the hostile environment of the upper atmosphere and some have travelled to the moon. Nevertheless, if the hypothesis is right, the global environment is still regulated by a process depending on such lowly creatures as micro-ogranisms and algae.

The viewpoint has profound implications and disturbs many of the assumptions underlying discussions of environmental issues and the idea of "Spaceship Earth", and it is probably worth while to make a small digression to consider them. It suggests that some of the human activities that disturb the environment will have less effect than would be predicted without regard to the regulation imposed by Gaia. However, there is no cause for complacency (Lovelock 1981), since regulation can presumably become overloaded at some point. In fact, Gaia may increase the danger by masking the effects of environmental disturbances until there is an abrupt breakdown. This probably would not destroy all life and with it Gaia herself; life has survived previous catastrophic changes including a shift from a reducing to an oxidizing atmosphere. However there is no reason to think that Gaia has any commitment to man as the dominant species.

To show how such control might be established, Lovelock discussed (as a 'parable') a simple model of a planet on which two species of plants ('daisies') can grow. One of these is dark in colour ('black', for convenience) and the other light ('white'). The spread of black daisies causes the planet to become warmer, whereas white daisies reflect radiation and cause it to become cooler. The bare ground of the planet has an albedo intermediate between those of the two species.

(The reference to 'daisies' caused some confusion when the idea was discussed internationally. The precise species, *bellis perennis*, is unimportant; it is simply one of the first to come to the mind of a native speaker of English asked to imagine a small flowering plant. In one sense it is an unfortunate choice for the present purpose since real daisies are almost all white.)

It is assumed, in the model, that the growth rate of daisies is a single-peaked function of temperature; the exact shape is not critical. An important point is that the function is exactly the same for both species, with the same optimal temperature. It is also assumed that the daisies have a death rate which is independent of temperature and is also the same for both species. It is assumed that the two species are sufficiently segregated in their growing areas that the local temperature for black daisies is higher than for white ones. The model includes simple and plausible assumptions about the thermal conductivity of the planet.

Computer simulation has shown that this simple model is effective in keeping the mean temperature of the planet close to the optimum for daisy-growth, over a wide range of levels of incident radiation. It is not difficult to explain the result—when the incident radiation is such that the equilibrium temperature of bare ground is *below* the optimum for growth, black daisies have an advantage since they are locally warmer. They therefore proliferate faster than the white variety and this causes warming of the planet as a whole. The converse applies when the incident radiation correpsonds to a bare-ground temperature *above* the optimum for growth.

Daisyworld has been termed a 'parable', presumably to encourage interpretations and analogies that lead well away from the original model. 'Daisies' can be replaced by anything having a rate of growth dependent on an environmental variable, and itself influencing the local value of the variable. The type of entity substituted need not be an entire living organism. It might, for example, be a form of *hypercycle* as postulated by Eigen and Schuster (1977, see also Jantsch 1980). It would be surprising if the origins of internal regulation in living systems could not be usefully represented by making some such substitutions for Lovelock's 'daisies'. The subsequent evolution of this capability, eventually resulting in complex 'intelligent' behaviour, is the subject of the present speculation.

3

Hidden Continuity

3.1 WHERE CONTINUITY LURKS

The purpose of this chapter is to consider relatively indirect ways in which continuity enters into AI. The distribution of topics between Chapters 2 and 3 is somewhat arbitrary, depending on subjective assessment of the degree to which particular manifestations of continuity are readily apparent. The arbitrariness supports the general contention that there is a connectionn between the various types of continuity, such that study of the obvious forms is likely to promote understanding of the others.

The discussion begins by considering the place of continuity in neural-network models, and goes on to discuss the acknowledgement of continuity that is implicit in Ashby's formalism. This leadds to consideration of the general principle of *heuristic connection*, and the types of similarity effective in some existing schemes. Finally, it argues that continuity plays a greater part in readily observed natural intelligence than is usually assumed.

3.2 NEURAL NETWORK MODELS

Neural models may be continuous or discrete at the cellular level. This is a simple distinction which might seem more appropriate to the preceding chapter. However, it is not a simple matter to examine the relationship between continuity at the cellular level and its effect in overall network behaviour.

In considering information processing in the nervous system, there is an old dilemma as to whether the neurons should be represented as discrete 'logical' elements or as continuous transducers. Living neurons make a discrete response by 'firing' under suitable conditions, and this is the basis of their communication function. A resting neuron has a potential of about 70 mV between its interior and exteror, with the interior negative. This is due to the differences in concentration of ions between the interior of the cell and its surroundings, and a mechanism termed the *sodium pump* prevents the two from coming into equilibrium by diffusion.

Excitation of a neuron, normally because of the activity of neighbouring neurons influencing it through *synapses*, requires that a certain amount of cell membrane becomes depolarized, i.e. ceases to have the potential difference across it. Once this happens, its permeability to the various ions changes in such a way that a current flows and affects neighbouring areas of membrane so that they also become depolarized. The result is that a wave of depolarization, or excitation, spreads over the entire surface of the cell. It is a transient effect, since in about a millisecond the polarization is re-established.

If the cell has a long *axon* the wave of depolarization runs along it. The fibres which run in bundles in the nerves of the body are cell axons, and they may be several metres long. The wave of depolarization is the *nerve impulse*. Since it is propagated by continuous excitation, rather like an explosion running along a trail of gunpowder, it travels much more slowly than signals in electric cables. Depending on the diameter and type of the fibre, the velocity of conduction may be anything from a few tens of centimetres per second up to about a hundred metres per second.

In primitive nervous systems it is possible that one, or a very few, *nerve impulses* may produce an observable effect. The apparent simplicity of events in primitive systems has made them attractive to neurophysiologists (Alkon and Farley 1984).

In the nervous systems of higher animals, however, the signals in nerve fibres are found to consist of trains of impulses, evenly spaced in time. Experimental neurophysiologists are themselves strongly conditioned to recognize such regularity (as an array of spikes on the oscilloscope screen, or a machine-gun-like rattle from an audio monitor) as they adjust the position of a micro-electrode to get a single-unit response. For a motor nerve, the higher the frequency the stronger is the muscle contraction. Similarly, for a nerve coming from a sense organ, the impulse frequency increases with increasing strength of stimulus. It is also strongly influenced by the rate of change of the stimulus.

For some sense organs the physical input has no obvious polarization from 'weak' to 'strong'. An example is the collection of receptors in a knee-joint that send signals to the central nervous system depending on the angle of the joint (Boyd and Roberts 1953; Andrew and Roberts 1954). It has been found that some receptors increase their frequency as the angle becomes more obtuse, while others go the other way. There is always a strong contribution depending on the rate of movement. Some receptors respond only to movement in a particular direction, while others give a response determined by the modulus of the angular velocity.

These findings, together with a vast amount of other experimenatal data, are consistent with the idea that transmission in nerves uses a form of pulse-frequency modulation. This can also be argued on the basis of the kown properties of individual neurons. As well as summing inputs spatially over the set of input synapses, neurons are able to integrate them in time. (Strictly, it is pseudo-integration, with a certain time-constant of decay.) They also readily generate chains of impulses whose frequency depends on membrane potential difference. A neuron can therefore be modelled as a transducer between continuous input signals and a continuous output one, all represented by impulse frequencies. The relationship between input and output is necessarily non-linear, since the output frequency has a lower bound of zero and an upper one determined by physical characteristics.

Hopfield (1982) briefly reviews these aspects in justifying his representation of a neuron as a transducer with a sigmoid response curve. This representation, employed also by Harth *et al* (1970), Wilson and Cowan (1972) and Fish (1981), is in contrast to the widely-accepted model as a threshold 'logical' device, commonly referred to as the *McCulloch-Pitts neuron*. To some extent the difference is one of connotation or context for the modeller, rather than of the physical nature of the model neuron, since Hopfield goes on to approximate the sigmoid response by a step-function, implying a return to the pure threshold device. Nevertheless, his subsequent analysis treats the neuron in a way that is more appropriate to a continuous transducer than to a logical element.

The idea of a neuron as a continuous transducer has existed for a long time, and even the original paper by McCulloch and Pitts (1943) was followed immediately by another (Landahl, McCulloch and Pitts 1943) showing that the 'logical' viewpoint could readily be modifed to refer to probabilities, and hence to averaged frequencies in neural paths.

McCulloch (1974) acknowledged that he had grown tired of hearing of the Pitts and McCulloch neuron, which had been widely accepted as a more literal model than had been intended. In a great deal of other discussion (e.g. McCulloch 1959) he emphasized the purpose of the model; it had a very crude correspondence to physiological reality and was only intended to demonstrate that a network of elements having this simplified version of real neurons had certain computational capabilities.

Despite these disclaimers, the model neuron has been widely accepted as a basis for neuro-modelling. A more serious defect than its lack of correspondence to real physiological neurons is the inherent assumption that discrete 'logical' (in sense A), operations are to be seen as fundamental. Undoubtedly the higher animals perform such 'logical' operations, but it is probably a mistake to look for them at the cellular level—this point will be considered later in this chapter and in Chapter 4. The quotes are used to indicate that 'logic' is intended in what was termed sense A in Chapter 1, namely the sense understood in computer technology and formal logic, in which continuity has no place.

Hopfield's treatment shows how a net of model neurons can satisfy the requirement for *associative memory*. An item to be stored is represented by a pattern of excitation of the net, i.e. by a partitioning of the total set of neurons into a set which is excited and a set that is quiescent. In the initial form of the model, all neurons are connected to all others, in both directions. Synaptic weights are adjusted in a plausible way to represent the correlation between the respective states of excitation of the two neurons joined by the synapse, the correlation being integrated over all the items to be stored.

Each neuron which is in its active state makes a contribution, equal to the appropriate synaptic weight, to the summation formed in each other neuron in the net. The state of excitation of individual neurons is revised at random intervals, with the same inter-revision interval for each neuron. In the revision, the summation in the neuron is compared with a threshold level, and if necessary the state of the neuron (excited or quiescent) is altered appropriately. Unlike the networks considered by McCulloch and Pitts, Hopfield's network is asynchronous.

Hopfield shows that, in such a net, the excitation patterns corresponding to stored items are *attractors*. That is to say, the state of the net converges on one or other of them. The particular attractor reached depends on the starting state of the net, and is that which is 'nearest' according to some criterion. This is the basis of an *associative memory*, since starting states which do not correspond to items in memory can be regarded as incomplete or distorted versions of the memorized items. The convergence is demonstrated by defining a quantity E which has a local minimum at each of the attractor states, and showing that every state-change of the network must reduce E.

Associative memory is an important aspect of neural processing and intelligence. Needless to say, it is only one aspect and much more is needed to account for the many capabilities that are denoted by 'intelligence', and particularly the problem-solving ability that is the primary concern of most work in AI. It is important to take a closer look at the type of similarity that is effective in allowing associative recall, and a return is made to this topic in section 3.5.1.

If the synaptic *weight* of the connection from neuron i to neuron j is denoted by T_{ij}, the postulated learning process produces the following result:

$$T_{ij} = \sum_{s}(2V_i^s - 1)(2V_j^s - 1) \qquad (1)$$

but with $T_{ii}=0$.

In this, the summation is over the set s of 'learned' states of the network, and V_i^s has value unity if neuron i is active in the state s, or zero otherwise. The expressions in round brackets in the summation represent the excitation states as values that are symmetrical about zero, i.e. $+1$ and -1 rather than 1 and 0. The expression is symmetrical in i and j, so $T_{ij} = T_{ji}$.

For any state s' of the network (whether one of the trained-in ones or not), the input to the i-th neuron is:

$$\sum_j T_{ij} V_j^{s'} = \sum_s (2V_i^s - 1)\left[\sum_j V_j^{s'}(2V_j^s - 1)\right] \tag{2}$$

where the summations with respect to j are over all other neurons in the net, and those with respect to s are over the set of trained-in states.

It is easy to see that the expected value of the expression within the square brackets is zero unless $s = s'$, in which case it is always positive. When this term is positive, the sign of the r.h.s. is determined by the earlier part of it, and hence the effect of the input is to reinforce the existing state of excitation of the i-th neuron.

The quantity E is defined by:

$$E = -\tfrac{1}{2}\sum\sum T_{ij} V_i V_j \tag{3}$$

where the double summation is over all pairs of values of i and j, such that $i \neq j$. It is easy to show that, when a particular V_i is altered in accordance with the algorithm, i.e. in the direction dictated by the sign of the r.h.s. of Eqn. (2), the corresponding change in E must be negative. This follows from the result of differentiation:

$$\Delta E = -\Delta V_i \sum_j T_{ij} V_j \tag{4}$$

in which the result of the summation is the input to the neuron determining its change of state, and hence of the same sign as the change ΔV_i by which it is multiplied.

It follows that E must have local minima corresponding to the stable states of the net. Changes in excitation determined by the adjustment algorithm must bring the net to one of these stable states. Provided the number of trained-in patterns is not too large, relative to the size of the net, the stable state reached corresponds, almost certainly, to a trained-in pattern.

A brief account of the theory, as well as references to some later developments, appears in the review paper of Hinton (1989). The result guarantees, with high probability, convergence of the net on a trained-in pattern. In this it has some correspondence to the convergence proof for the *perceptron training algorithm* (Nilsson 1965), but with the important difference that the latter applies only to a network having no closed loops of connection paths. Hinton mentions that the final convergence on a stable state of a Hopfield net may be complicated by the fact that the minimum may lie in a long narrow valley. (In this he is speaking loosely about geometrical features of high-dimensional space, as is customary in connection with numerical optimization procedures.) The result is that the final convergence procedure may be slow and may not be to the minimum that is nearest according to a simple criterion. A possible remedy is discussed by Hinton. In my own experiments (Andrew 1990b) it was found that the convergence was less robust than the original presentation suggests, and further investigation is clearly needed.

3.2.1 Continuity in Neural Nets

It is probably a fair comment that the achievement of a greater level of 'intelligence' in neural nets has been associated with a shift of emphasis from purely 'logical' operation to operations of a continuous nature. In their original paper, McCulloch and Pitts considered model neurons having fixed excitation thresholds and synaptic weights, since their aim was simply to examine the computational capabilities of networks of such elements. In most later work, continuously-variable weights have been assumed, particularly since there is evidence that the effectiveness of synapses in living nervous systems is modified by experience.

It has been mentioned that some form of continuity is implicit in any form of learning or adaptation or evolution. It need not take the form of synaptic-weight variation; a simple way to demonstrate this is to reflect that the findings of McCulloch and Pitts show that any learning scheme that can be programmed on a general-purpose digital computer can also be realized in a network of fixed-parameter model neurons. Adaptive networks composed of fixed-parameter neurons have been described by George (1973, 1976) as *belief networks* and prove the point. They embody a form of continuity 'in the large' since their set of states is ordered so that its members correspond to different strengths of belief.

The work of Hopfield, and other neuromodellers mentioned above, goes further in the direction of introducing continuity, since the neuron is represented as a continuous non-linear transducer. Hopfield then retracts a little from this position when he approximates the sigmoid transducer response by a step-function, and arranges that changes in the state of excitation of a neuron occur as discrete events.

These deviations from truly-continuous operation give a model that lends itself to computer simulation. Simulation is important in justifying the theory, because the argument in terms of the quantity E (an analogy with solid-state physics) depends, initially, on an assumption that all synaptic connections are formed symmetrically—if neuron i influences neuron j through a synapse of weight w, then neuron j must be similarly connected to neuron i. It can be argued informally, and can be confirmed by simulation, that the important property of the network survives when the symmetry condition is relaxed. The essential property is the existence of the trained-in stable attractor states.

Although the final model as described by Hopfield is discontinuous, its derivation is as a net of continuous transducers. A program has been written (Andrew 1990b) which allows comparison of, on the one hand, Hopfield's method of adjustment, and on the other a true continuous simulation. The continuous simulation is deterministic, whereas Hopfield's method has some stochastic character since neurons submit randomly to revision of their states of excitation. It has, however, been verified that the interesting network properties are similar under the two kinds of adjustment, though, as mentioned above, convergence of both is less robust than was expected.

Some considerations that conflict with the model of an individual neuron as a continuous transducer are reviewed by Sejnowski (1986), extending an argument by Marr (1982). These workers refer to the short time required by the nervous system to perform complex recognition tasks. It can be shown that the time required is between 200 and 300 milliseconds. For neurons, this limits the processing to an absolute maximum of 300 serial steps, equivalent to a very modest digital computer program. It is remarkable that complex processing is achieved with such limited *computational depth*.

The claim that this would be a rather modest program for the purpose requires some justification. No attempt will be made here to develop a quantitative argument, but it is worth mentioning that the computational steps are counted at the CPU or logic-element level, so a great many would be involved in executing a single instruction of a high-level language. Also, the computational tasks correspond to advanced forms of scene analysis whose achievement in computer programs requires rather tedious processes such as labelling of edges.

It is accepted in the Sejnowski-Marr discussion that continuous variables have to be processed, if only because visual recognition certainly takes account of gradations of brightness. On the other hand, if continuous variables are represented by pulse frequencies, individual computational steps must take much longer than one millisecond, since input frequency must be sampled over several impulses and output frequency must be established by generating a similar number.

Marr relates the minimum processing time for a computational step to the precision of computation, and shows that a very modest level of precision requires that the processing time be at least 50 milliseconds. This, of course, is unacceptable according to the present argument since it would mean that the *computational depth*, already startlingly low at 200 or 300, would fall to 2% of that value.

Marr's argument about processing time embodies an assumption that pulse frequency is effectively estimated by an integrative process, as is required if the modulation is truly of average frequency and not of pulse-interval. An electronic instrument to estimate pulse frequency as the reciprocal of pulse-interval was demonstrated by Andrew and Roberts (1953, 1954) with the argument that its response to frequency changes was as rapid as theoretically possible. However, its mode of operation is not acceptable as a model of a neuron, and any plausible alternative supports Marr's contention.

The only other possibility seems to be to suppose that a continuous quantity is represented by the number of neurons firing simultaneously rather than by discharge frequency in any single neuron. For a single neuron, the instantaneous value of the quantity determines the probability of firing. Sejnowski quotes experimental data lending additional support to this view, which is essentially that of Landahl, McCulloch and Pitts (1943).

This viewpoint is not entirely consistent with the representation, by Hopfield and others, of a neuron as a continuous transducer element. The conflict is resolved if the reference to a continuous transducer is assumed to apply to a group of neurons receiving similar inputs and generating an output represented by the firing rate summed over the group. It is, of course, not necessary that the representation be exactly the same throughout the nervous system—the representation of continuous variables could be mainly as spatial density of excitation where fast processing is important, and mainly by pulse frequency, corresponding to temporal density of excitation, elsewhere.

It is paradoxical that the challenge to the interpretation of a neuron as a continuous transducer arose from consideration of the requirement for continuous-variable processing. The assertion that continuity enters in *some* fundamental way is unchallenged!

3.3 STATE-DETERMINED BEHAVIOUR

Ashby (1956, 1960) gave a new formalism for the representation of *systems* in general, with particular application to living systems. A *system* is an abstraction, or a set of variables recognized as being relevant for some particular purpose. Systems are often referred to by the name of the physical object on which they are imposed, but it is important to remember that the system is not identical with the object. Ashby (1956), quoted by Klir (1985), illustrates this by reference to a simple pendulum which, as a system, is represented by a very small number of variables. However, these are selected from a vast number that could be specified for a real pendulum. As Ashby puts it:

> "The real pendulum . . . has also mass, temperature, electric conductivity, crystalline structure, chemical impurities, some radioactivity . . ."

The instantaneous state of a pendulum, as a system, is represented by two variables, namely the angle of deflection and the angular velocity. These define a point in a two-dimensional phase-space, and knowledge of the physics of the situation make it possible to draw trajectories, or *lines of behaviour* in the phase-space. The line of behaviour does not fully represent the system unless it is marked along its length to show unit intervals of time, but the representation is sufficient for most purpses with the time-scale omitted. Since the line of behaviour specifies the state of the system at any future time, given its current state, the system is *state-determined.*

Naturally, the system is only state-determined in the absence of external disturbances. Strictly if the system includes *all* relevant variables there can be no such thing as an external disturbance. However, it is often convenient to consider a set of variables that is not totally closed in this way, so that external inputs can occur. For example, if a simple pendulum is occasionally and unpredictably tapped with a hammer, it may be simplest to retain the system representation which ignores the hammer, and to regard each tap as causing a jump to a new *behaviour line.*

3.3.1 Automaton Theory

An alternative representation of state-determined behaviour is that denoted by *automaton theory*, and reviewed by numerous authors including Minsky (1967) and Andrew (1983). It has already been outlined in the discussion of *learning* in section 1.3. The difference between this representation and that of Ashby is, essentially, that Ashby recognizes a form of continuity. The phase-space representation implies continuity, at least 'in the large' as specified here.

Ashby (1956) comments on this aspect, where he says (p.32):

> "For numbers can be used cardinally as well as ordinally, that is, they may be used as mere labels without any reference to their natural order. Such are the numberings of the divisions of an army, and of the subscribers on a telephone system; for the subscriber whose number is, say, 4051 has no particular relation to the subscriber whose number is 4052: the number identifies him but does not relate him."

In spite of this, Ashby was often anxious to maintain that continuity was unimportant in his theoretical treatment. For example, he says (Ashby 1967):

"As its concepts are initially quite free from an implication of either continuity, or of order, or of metric, or of linearity (though in no way excluding them), the method can be applied to the facts of biology without the facts having to be distorted for purely mathematical reasons."

In the same discussion, and elsewhere, he attached much importance to the work on *set theory* of the French group using the pseudonym of Bourbaki, since this showed how mathematics could be divorced from continuity. For an English-language presentation of the relevant theory he used to recommend Birkoff and MacLane (1953). He also welcomed with enthusiasm the advent of digital computers as providing a useful model for understanding brain function, but gave a slightly misleading picture of computers as being purely 'logical' devices. Of course, as already discussed here, from one point of view they are purely 'logical' since the basic operations are on binary digits, but the principle of continuity is quite firmly embedded in both the hardware and the software. Ashby's representation of brain function was more continuous than he liked to think.

3.4 THE ASHBY-BELLMAN DEBATE

These matters received an airing at a very early stage in the development of AI, at a meeting in Evanston, Illinois, in 1963 (Ashby 1964; Bellman 1964), though unfortunately the spirit of controversy does not come through strongly in the printed proceedings. Ashby gave a Keynote Address, in which he suggested that a good way to stimulate progress in the following ten years would be to promote a major effort to make a chess-playing machine to beat the human world champion.

Bellman contested this view on the grounds that chess operates in a highly-artificial environment quite different from that in which biological intelligence has evolved. In particular, the chess environment lacks the continuity that allows convergence on a solution. Most tasks, in the everyday, practical environment, have a different character. The discovery of a procedure for baking a palatable loaf of bread, for example, was undoubtedly achieved by producing a succession of loaves that were sub-optimal though not totally unacceptable.

There are senses in which both Ashby and Bellman were right, and it is interesting to consider how. If we ignore for the moment the very puzzling phenomenon of prodigies who take to chess like ducks to water, most chess-players do in fact develop their skill by practice in a way that is not unlike the baker's gradual improvement of his particular skill. Although the selection of a move, or a sequence of moves, appears to a non-player to be a task in which the smallest deviation leads to unqualified (and unquantifiable) disaster, chess players have somehow imposed continuous criteria on the task environment. They can, for example, perceive similarities between alternative gambits. The term *heuristic connection*, as already mentioned, was coined by Minsky (1959b, 1963) to refer to these intangible, but vital criteria of problem similarity.

In a sense, therefore, Ashby was right, since the study of chess could reveal the types of heuristic connection that would bring the task within the domain acceptable to Bellman. On the other hand, this does not seem to be what Ashby had in mind, and Bellman is probably right in claiming that a better starting-point is a task environment in which continuous critera are more evident (as they are in baking). Certainly, the evolution of natural intelligence has progressed from task environments in which continuity is evident, to those like chess-playing or mathematical theorem-proving in which it is effective but well hidden.

3.5 ANALOGY

The type of criterion denoted by *heuristic connection* is necessary for the operation of any form of reasoning by *analogy*. In fact, the two terms are virtually interchangeable, except for the possible distinction that the phenomena denoted by analogy are restricted to those manifestations of the utilization of heuristic connection that are relatively accessible to introspection. The study of analogy is certainly a currently-popular topic of AI study.

An early paper by MacKay (1959), already quoted in Chapter 1, sums up the argument for saying that analogy depends on continuity. Discussing how the brain succeeds in forming hypotheses that are likely to be fruitful, he argues:

> "The evidence [on which the hypothesis is formed] itself must be embodied in such a physical form that unforseeable but reasonable hypotheses or bright ideas have a better-than-average chance of spontaneously *growing* out of their embodiment ... the physical state representing a good idea is 'near' (in the sense of statistical mechanics) to the state representing that data, and that of most useless ideas 'remote' .... This would seem to demand the use of *analogue/* methods of representation ... "

He is careful to say that the idea of '*analogue*' representation should not be interpreted so literally as to imply physical three-dimensional models in the nervous system. It is perhaps unfortunate that the term *analogue*, or *analog*, has come to denote a particular form of hardware representation, rather than any representation that acknowledges continuity. It is the latter interpretation that is important for AI.

3.5.1 Heuristic Connection

Although the principle of heuristic connection was enunciated so many years ago, it is difficult to point to any system that can be said to exploit it in the general way that Minsky visualized. A variety of different types of similarity are exploited by existing systems, as reviewed in the next section, but natural intelligence seems to have a special facility for seeking, or recognizing, new forms of connection.

The type of continuous criterion implicit in the principle is also needed for operation of the *basic learning heuristic* (Minsky and Selfridge 1961) and the idea of *mutated fission* in a *pandemonium* (Selfridge 1959), as mentioned in section 2.8. The difficulty of implementing the latter is illustrated by the fact that a practical device for character recognition described by Selfridge and Neisser (1963) is essentially a pandemonium but there is no implementation of mutated fission. Nevertheless, in a restricted context, Forsyth (1981; also Forsyth and Rada 1986) was able to embody a simple form of the principle in a version of *pandemonium* to which he gave the name *Beagle* to emphasize the connection with biological evolution as propounded by Darwin.

An example of the failure of an intended self-organizing scheme is the approach of Friedberg (1958, and Friedberg *et al* 1959), discussed by Minsky (1963). In the scheme computer programs were randomly modified until a particular goal was achieved. The scheme was successful in producing programs to perform very simple tasks, but the amount of effort needed was greater than if new programs had been formed randomly. The failure can be attributed to the lack of a suitable form of heuristic connection between program versions. Selfridge met the same problem in considering mutated fission in a *pandemonium*, and wrote:

> "At present we plan to pick one subdemon [essentially a feature detector] and alter some of his parameters more or less at random. This will usually require that we reduce the subdemon himself to some canonical form so that the random changes we insert do not have the effect of rewriting the program so that it will not run or so that it will enter a closed loop without any hope of getting out of it."

The versatility of the brain in detecting subtle connections, or kinds of similarity, is beautifully and wittily illustrated by examples in Hofstadter's Forword to the book by Kanerva (1988). He draws his examples mainly from the use of language, and particularly of idiomatic phrases which are readily accepted in modified forms. For example, the phrase 'turning a blind eye' has a meaning, with nuances, that is readily carried over to a similar one referring to a 'deaf ear', and even the phrase 'turning the other eye' has been known to emerge as a hybrid with the Biblical reference to 'turning the other cheek'. Hofstadter gives other examples of such modifications and hybridizations.

It is generally believed, at least by people who went to school in Britain, that the original 'turning of a blind eye' was by Nelson during a particular sea battle, when he put a telescope to his blind eye and was able to say with truth "I see no signal". The imagery is a little difficult to carry over to the modified versions of the phrase, but the acquired associations and nuances survive independently of it.

The point made by Hofstadter is of course entirely valid, but it is perhaps unfortunate that compelling illustrations are most readily found in the context of linguistic communication. Such communication must have been a relatively late evolutionary development, and the associational capabilities that are illustrated are presumably pre-linguistic in origin. Subtle discriminations are involved in visual processing, for example in indentifying particular plants by their leaves, of recognizing faces, or interpreting facial expressions and other kinds of 'body language'. Subtle discriminations play an important part in the social interaction of animals, and it is even possible that modern man has lost some capabilities in these directions as a price paid for increased 'encephalization'.

3.5.2 Types of Similarity

So far, the idea of heuristic connection, or of 'some criterion of similarity' as implied by the *basic learning heuristic*, has been discussed in the abstract. There are, however, various schemes that embody a concrete realization of such a criterion, and some of these will now be reviewed. It is easy to have the feeling that none of the computed criteria has the generality or subtlety that is needed to solve non-trivial problems, though it is possible that some suitable combination of many simple criteria could be enormously more powerful than any single one of them.

Some criterion of pattern similarity is implicit in any scheme for pattern classification, since there has to be some respect in which patterns belonging to the same class are more alike than patterns belonging to distinct classes. For many schemes, the 'best match' between an incoming pattern and a prototype is defined very simply in terms of either maximizing a correlation function of minimizing a *Hamming distance*. The latter is a count of the number of discrepancies between two sets of yes/no receptors.

Where a simple criterion of this sort is evaluated on the basis of the states of excitation of primary detectors (e.g. the light-sensitive elements of a retina), it is an example of template-matching, and unlikely to be useful for anything beyond the recognition of printed characters conforming to an approximately-known font, after pre-processing to standardize the position.

When a simple criterion of pattern similarity is applied with respect to the responses of elements which may be termed *feature detectors*, the situation changes greatly. Practical character-classification devices operate in exactly this way, as discussed in early work by Selfridge and Neisser (1963), Parks (1969) and many others. The idea was explicitly embodied in Steinbuch's *Lernmatrix* (Steinbuch 1961; Steinbuch and Piske 1963).

Devices analogous to the reconstruction of a visual image by holographic techniques have been musch discussed by Gabor (1968), Longuet-Higgins (1968) and others. The fact that missing elements may be 'inferred' in the reconstruction suggests a model of *associative recall* or even *inductive inference*. Uttley's *conditional probability computer* (Uttley 1956, 1959) allowed for such inference as an extension of the idea of yhe Pavlovian *conditioned reflex*. The criterion of similarity that is effective in these devices is essentially of the Hamming-distance type, allowing an incomplete pattern to be filled-in to agree with the stored one it otherwise closely matches. The interest of the devices stems from the biological plausibility of their mechanisms rather than any subtlety of their overall behaviour.

It is somewhat disappointing to find, after the enthusiastic introduction by Hofstadter, that the treatment by Kanerva (1988) is on the assumption that elements to be stored in memory can all be represented as vectors of binary digits, with no effective criterion of similarity except Hamming distance. He is, however, careful to explain that the binary digits correspond to the outputs of feature detectors, and goes on to discuss how these could come to be set up.

The paper of Hopfield (1982) also regards memory items as vectors of binary digits, correponding to instantaneous states of excitation of neurons in a network. Again the criterion of similarity is of the Hamming-distance type, though not precisely specified. (The network, as has been mentioned, has a set of stable states, corresponding to memory items, and these act as *attractors*, such that the network state is likely to move towards one of them from an arbitrary starting-point.) The effective criterion of similarity, referred to the real world, is a rather fortuitous function of the network connections.

Obviously, when a simple criterion of similarity is used in conjunction with feature detectors relating it to the real world, the effective criterion of similarity is strongly dependent on the nature of the feature detectors. In fact, the main task of any learning or self-organizing system is to form a suitable set of feature detectors, and this was the problem that Oliver Selfridge (1959) sought to illuminate by introducing his *pandemonium* paradigm. Kanerva also tackles the problem, but in a way that does not seem to add much to earlier treatments.

When discussing interactions with an unspecified 'outside world', it is easy to fall into a simplistic stimulus-response viewpoint which is not necessarily profitable. One of the original messages of the book by Minsky and Papert (1969) is that the perceptron approach is not necessarily the best for studying interesting problems of perception. They advocate instead the approach now denoted by *scene analysis*, then represented by the pioneering work of Guzman on the analysis of line pictures of polyhedral objects.

Scene analysis depends on representations of the kind that have been found useful in a great deal of AI work—lists of objects (faces, edges, intersections), and relationships between them. Data structures allowing such representations are familiar in modern computer science and were initially developed in the AI context. *Directed graphs* allow a convenient display of such structures for human examination , either on the computer screen or the printed page. Some abstract concepts can be represented by such linked lists, or, equivalently, by directed graphs. For example, Winston (1975, 1980, 1984) has pointed out that, in the context of an environment in which objects are built from simple shapes like blocks and wedges, an 'arch' is formed by two blocks standing on end, with a horizontal block or wedge on top of both of them.

The concept of 'arch' is fairly easily represented as a linked list or directed graph, and computer programs have been written to deduce such representations from examples. It has to be possible to label objects with properties like 'vertical' and 'horizontal', and to represent relationships like 'on top of', 'in front of', or 'touching'. The program to form the representation can be said to learn the concept of an 'arch'.

It is necessary also to represent negative relationships such as 'not touching', and in addition to being shown examples of 'arches', the learning program has to be shown other assemblies that are not arches because the two upright members touch.

Obviously, the concept of an 'arch' described here is an enormous simplification of the human idea of an arch, even when restricted to assemblies that could be formed in the blocks world. As described it deals only with discrete yes/no concepts such as the relationship of 'touching', but the human idea of an arch would be violated if the upright blocks were 'nearly touching', and it is probably necessary to invoke the formalism of *fuzzy set theory* (Zadeh 1983). However, the general method of representation is clearly of wide applicability and facilities for using it have been built into a system termed, appropriately, ARCHES (Chouraqui 1985). It has potential application wherever empirical knowledge is treated, and Chouraqui mentions as examples the fields of law, medicine, social sciences, economics and archaeology.

The use of linked lists, as in ARCHES, allows a new type of criterion of similarity to be employed. The attempt can be made to match one graph with another, and if part of one graph is unknown it is possible to decide how it could be filled in to preserve the match. Chouraqui has used this as the basis for a model of reasoning by analogy, since if the graphs match well in other areas it is 'reasonable' to guess that the unknown part matches also. It is not difficult to devise a numerical evaluation of goodness of match of two representations, though presumably the weights to be attached to different kinds of mismatch must be application-dependent.

A somewhat similar technique has been applied by Carbonell (1984) to supplement the technique of *means-ends analysis* which is the basis of the *general problem solver* of Newell, Shaw and Simon (1959). Here the stored object is an *episodic memory* of the steps taken to obtain a solution to a particular problem. If, then, another problem is presented having some similarity to the earlier one, it may be possible to modify the episodic memory appropriately, so as to obtain a solution more economically than by working again through the full GPS procedure. Here again an attempt at matching has to be made, this time of the two problem statements. If one statement can be transformed to the other by a particular substitution, it may be possible to substitute correspondingly throughout the episodic memory, and so to solve the problem wih relatively little effort.

The reason that Forsyth (1981) was able to implement a form of mutated fission in a variant of Selfridge's *pandemonium* was that he restricted his attention to logical predicates. Within this restricted context there are fairly simple criteria of similarity and hence possibilities for small experimental changes. If the predicate is represented as a tree structure, the criteria of similarity are very like those computed with reference to other data structures in the foregoing.

Another interesting early development was *evolutionary programming*, the basis of the *simulated evolution* of Fogel, Owens and Walsh (1966). The current state of the evolving intelligent entity, and its experimental variations, were represented in the formalism of *finite automata*, which can again be represented by appropriately-labelled directed graphs. In the graphs the nodes represent automaton states, and the directed arcs the possible state transitions. It is not difficult to devise ways of making small alterations to such graphs, e.g. by adding or removing a node, or an arc, or changing the starting-state, or modifying the symbols indicating outputs. Some simple criteria of automaton similarity are implicit in these changes, and are the basis of the evolutionary process studied by these workers.

Similarity criteria for comparison of data strctures are implicit, sometimes merely as rules for making small experimental changes, in the work of Winston, Chouraqui, Carbonell, Forsyth, and of Fogel, Owens and Walsh. On the whole the criteria are rather simple and it is difficult to imagine the capabilities described by Hofstadter emerging purely on such a basis. Before leaving the topic, however, two points should be noted, as follows:

(a) Even simple criteria may be surprisingly powerful when used in combination. An example of this can be seen in the work of Andreae and Andreae (1978) on a recognition task. The requirement is to recognize certain sequences of symbols in an input string, but the string may contain irrelevant extra symbols (e.g. hiccoughs form a speaker), and so may the sample sequences. It is not known in advance whether hiccoughs are irrelevant, but it is realized that they are in some way different from the other symbols. A solution is to have several recognition systems working in parallel, one matching the full sequences, another matching without regard to hiccoughs, and so on, and if any one of these recognizers detects a match it assumes control and triggers an output signal. This is of course a very simple idea, but the general principle, of many computations proceeding in parallel until one achieves agreement with the input, is very much in accordance with current ideas on neural processing.

(b) Even at this simple level it is possible to illustrate the importance of making a suitable choice of similarity criterion. For many purposes, two algebraic expressions, or data structures, are similar if one can be obtained from the other by making some substitution throughout. In fact, if the variable is bound within an expression, the substitution may be irrelevant. On the other hand, the meaning of an expression can be totally altered by substituting for only some of the occurrences of a variable while leaving the rest unchanged. According to a simple lexical or Hamming-distance-like criterion of similarity, however, the expressions are more alike with only some substitutions than with all occurrences substituted.

Since the first draft of this book was prepared, a comprehensive review of approaches to analogical reasoning has been published (Hall 1989). The overall conclusions are in general agreement with those presented here, but it is interesting to note that techniques for dealing with analogy have been supplemented by the introduction of two continuous criteria. One of these is termed *salience* and the other *prototypicality*. Introspection readily supports the idea that the forming of analogies is governed by estimates of the suitability of the *source* structure for useful analogical manipulation; it is plausible to refer to this as the *salience* of the structure. The term *prototypicality* is applied to the corresponding property of the target structure, namely its readiness to be usefully extended by analogy. Although the types of analogy that have been utilized in AI programs can be described fairly simply in terms of correspondence, between data structures, continuous heuristic criteria have been invoked to guide the transformations that can usefully be made.

3.6 LANGUAGE AND JOKES

The importance of continuity in intelligence, and hence in AI, has been argued from various points of view. Perhaps it should have been seen as obvious from the start, and illustrated by the number of words of the language that have connotations of continuity. The very fact that the language makes provision for comparative and superlative versions of adjectives and adverbs shows an innate awareness of contintuity that is not captured by assigning yes/no values to predicates like 'is bigger than'. Neither is it captured by talking about the degree of membership of the fuzzy set of big objects, although fuzzy set theory goes some way to supplementing conventional 'logic' so as to acknowledge continuity.

Words that have obvious connotations of continuity include the terms that enter into physics and mensuration, like length, mass and volume, but also a great many others like comfort, exasperation, affection, incongruity, erudition. Many of these have connotations so delicate that no English-language term will suffice, and words from other languages, like *bonhomie, sang froid,* or *Gemütlichkeit* are felt to be the *mot juste.*

A great deal of attention has been given to possible methods of concept-formation (Bruner, Goodnow and Austin 1956; Hunt, Marin and Stone 1966). Pask (1959, 1962, 1975) has argued that the term *learning* should only be applied to processes which introduce new words in a language, thereby allowing a more concise and powerful reprerentation than was previously possible. With a suitable meaning attached to 'language', he virtually equates learning and concept-formation.

Pask uses the term *learning* to refer to any communication formalism including, for example, coding in neural pathways. The establishment and use of a concept need not depend on giving it a name in a spoken language. Pask observes that the evolution and persistence of concepts is similar to other forms of biological evolution; a concept must prove its worth in order to survive.

Unfortunately, when considering these ideas, it is usual to think of a *concept* as the means of recognizing discrete objects. Obviously, primitive man had to be able to recognize sabre-toothed tigers and edible plants, but it was also important to recognize whether the tiger was frustrated because she had failed to find other prey that day, and whether the edible plant was within reach or too high on a rock face to be gathered. The formation of quantifiable concepts like those of *height* and *frustration* has been largely ignored.

That concept-formation is not simply a matter of stimulus-response learning has been acknowledged by, for example, Wittgenstein, quoted by Dreyfus (1965). As he says, if we point to a table and say "brown", there is no simple way a child can know whether we mean that the name of that class of object is 'brown' (as opposed to 'table'), or that that particular example is called 'brown' (like 'Mr. Brown'), or that 'brown' is an attribute of the object, shared by many others. Yet somehow the normal developing child finally sorts out class names, proper names and attributes as well as various other possibilities.

It is also possible to point to the table and say 'heavy' or 'precious', perhaps reinforcing the idea by indicating an item of doll's house furniture and saying 'not heavy', or pointing to an old kitchen table and saying 'not precious'. The child learns to use these quantifiable attributes, but this aspect of concept formation tends to be neglected in general discussions. In some of its more tangible forms the later development of the use of continuous concepts has been studied by Piaget and his followers (Elkind and Flavell 1969) as *conservation*, but this starts from an assumption that the concepts already have some meaning.

Lenat (1984) lists the following as one of his heuristic rules with very general applicability:

"Examine extreme cases".

He has demonstrated the usefulness of this in his AM and EURISKO programs applied to mathematical discovery. It is, in fact, one of the most powerful of the heuristics he uses. It is easy to see that, once integer division, with a remainder, has been defined, the heuristic focusses attention on the extreme case where the remainder is zero and so the concept of *exact divisibility* is formed. A rather obvious next step (triggered in the program by other heuristics) is to examine positive integers and to count for each the number of exact divisors. The extreme lower value here is one, corresponding to the special case of the number one. Since this is a class with only one member it is probably interesting to look at the class of numbers giving the next lowest value, namely two, and thus the concept of *prime number* arises.

Lenat argues that some very general heuristic rules, including this one, play an important part in much intelligent activity as well as in biological evolution. For this particular rule to operate it is necessary to have some innate appreciation of continuity, otherwise the adjective *extreme* has no meaning.

An interesting insight into the nature of thought processes is given by what is found to be amusing. Jokes often depend on subtle associations of the kind reviewed by Hofstadter (Kanerva 1988), particularly when they produce networks of connections with some internal consistency though distinct from the chains of reasoning used in thinking seriously about the real world. It is because there is a close connection between humour and effective communication (and hence internal representations of knowledge) that many comments on writing style, e.g. in the book *Publishing with Ellis Horwood* (Sowan and Horwood 1987), are simultaneously witty and apposite.

It is interesting that there are many jokes that reveal an interest in the type of *extreme case* referred to by Lenat. An example appears in the review by Hofstadter, where the colloquial phrase 'not batting an eyelid', indicating extreme imperturbability, becomes amusing when it is made more extreme as 'not batting an eyelash'. There is in fact a whole class of jokes referred to as 'shaggy dog stories' which provide some amusement because the anecdotes themselves approach the upper limit of length and complexity permitted by the patience of teller and listener.

It is possible to find other examples of 'extreme case' jokes, but since those that come to mind lack the terseness of Hofstadter's example they will not be recounted. Their existence supports Lenat's assertion that the 'extreme cases' heuristic is important in human thought. This in turn further underlines the importance of continuity 'in the large'.

It is clear that natural language allows the communication of continuous concepts, and that both jokes and mathematical discovery indicate their utilization. This observation is consistent with the evolutionary viewpoint advocated here, and strengthens the case for it. Evolutionary aspects are discussed more fully in the next chapter.

4

Evolution

4.1 THE CONCEPT OF A CONCEPT

A number of reasons have been advanced for believing that continuity 'in the large' is important in intelligence, and hence in AI. This is also argued by Churchland (1986), who refers to the work of Pellionisz (1986, 1988) on the analysis of neural activity in terms of tensors. Intelligence also has discrete aspects, and the brain seems to combine the two with a degree of intimacy that has not been imitated in artifacts.

One of the difficulties facing any discussion of these matters is, of course, the fact that the brain can apply itself to tasks of many different kinds. Consequently, anyone trying to defend a pet theory or viewpoint can focus on particular aspects of brain function that lend support to it. It could be argued that Churchland and Pellionisz focus unduly strongly on matters of motor control and internal regulation, particularly the former since the argument is illustrated by reference to geometrical representation of the outside world and control of a hypothetical sensory robot.

At the same time, it can be argued that philosophers and AI workers have shown the opposite bias in focussing on essentially concept-based processing.

It is common to assume that the two areas of attention can be considered independently of each other. This assumption is contested by Churchland (her p.451) in the paragraph quoted in Chapter 1. The kind of nervous system activity needed for motor control and internal regulation is readily dismissed as 'primitive', and consequently uninteresting from an AI point of view. It is 'primitive' in the sense that it plays a larger part in the activity of primitive creatures than in that of higher ones (of which we usually consider ourselves to be the ultimate), but it is important at all levels.

The way to form a unified picture is presumably to consider the evolution of the tendency to operate in terms of discrete concepts. This tendency has itself the characteristics of a (pre-linguistic) concept, and has been aphorized (Andrew 1981) as the *concept of a concept*.

It has been argued by Pask (1975) that the formation and retention of concepts is like other kinds of biological evolution, and a concept has to prove its worth in order to survive. Much the same idea is put forward by Kochen (1981) who talkes of a *concept-niche*, analogous to an *ecological niche*. It is worth noting, parenthetically, that recent discussion (Galopin 1989; Andrew 1990a) stressing the 'systems' character of the idea of *ecological niche*, applies with equal force to that of *concept niche*.

To examine the evolutionary aspects it is necessary that a concept is understood in a wider sense than that of most formal definitions. In this it is not necessary that the system using the concept be able to name it in any language permitting communication outside itself. For example, the observations of Darwin (1897) on the behaviour of earthworms pulling leaf-like objects into their burrows, and the findings of Lettvin *et al* (1959) on the frog retina, both provide evidence for processing which can only be satisfactorily described in terms of concepts. However, the worms and frogs were effectively using concepts long before they were given spoken-language names by Darwin and Lettvin.

The observations on earthworms show them to be able to distinguish relevant features of the shape of objects, so that they grasp leaves by the more pointed end to drag them into their burrows, even though the more pointed end may be either the stem end or the distal end, depending on the type of leaf. Darwin confirmed his generalization by introducing artificial 'leaves' cut from paper.

The foregoing is true for the frog visual system if Lettvin's bold interpretation of the experimental results is accepted, but it should be mentioned that Gaze and Jacobson (1963) have presented a somewhat different viewpoint. It has been argued elsewhere (Andrew 1980, 1989) that this kind of descriptive ambiguity is likely to be characteristic of interesting evolutionary developments. The fact that certain retinal receptive units can be described in relatively prosaic geometric terms by Gaze and Jacobson does not necessarily invalidate their functional interpretation as 'bug-detectors'.

For the present purpose the most useful definition of a *concept* is in terms of the already-mentioned work of Pask (1962). He viewed the perception of concepts as the translation of sensory messages from a low-level source language to a meta-language, a concept being a symbol in the meta-language. The symbol must convey something which cannot be expressed in the source language, though specific examples can. In the frog-vision example, the primary receptors (rods and cones) are communicating in a source language as they signal their states of excitation to ganglion cells, including the subdivision of the latter that can be termed *bug-detectors*. There is no unique symbol in this language that indicates the probable presence of a fly, but the output of a 'bug-detector' is in a meta-language which justifies this term since it gives an indication of bug-detection.

The special sense in which the term *language* is used here, not necessarily implying the syntactic structure of a spoken language, is discussed by Arbib (1970).

4.2 SUCCINCTNESS

It is widely accepted that normal human communication is facilitated by *succinctness*, or the capacity for conveying essential information effectively and economically. The general view is elaborated by a great deal of discussion under the heading of *Occam's razor*, the reference being to the philosopher William of Ockham who was born in Ockham, Surrey, around 1280 and lived until about 1348. It is unlikely that he would recognize his original declaration, made in a theological context, in its modern elaborations. The term has become a convenient label for arguments stressing descriptive brevity.

All empirical science can be seen as the attempt to form succinct representations of a large mass of sensory data, and as such it is a formalization and extension of everyday learning. The colloquial meaning attached to *succinct* is 'short and to the point'. The stipulation of being 'to the point' implies the existence of a criterion of utility or worth.

The point is discussed by Gaines (1977) in connection with *system identification*, with reference to an argument between two advocates of respective models. One may claim "My model is a better approximation", but the other may make the counter-claim "But mine is a far *simpler* model. Indeed, I am not sure that all yours does is not just to retain a *memory* of the behaviour, whereas mine, whilst a worse approximation, is clearly a far better representation." (Gaines also gives a scholarly review of the relationship of these considerations to various philosophical viewpoints.)

The hypothetical argument brings out the point that succinctness is desirable, not only for the immediate economy of information storage or transmission capacity it achieves, but also because the concise representation is likely to be more useful. It may represent a general rule, agreeing with fresh sets of observations as well as the set from which it was derived, and perhaps allowing useful prediction. Although the disputants quoted by Gaines refer to *models*, the same considerations apply when alternative representations are not obviously formulated as models. As was discussed in Chapter 2, it is not a simple matter to define a *model*, and a rule for interacting with an environment, to satisfy some goal, automatically mirrors certain features of that environment and may be interpreted as embodying a model of them.

The term *succinct* has been used by Banerji (1969) in the AI context, and practical techniques to increase the succinctness of representations are dicussed by Rothenberg (1975). In a simple way, the goal of conciseness is implicit in schemes for automatic algebraic simplification and for the minimzation of other structures such as LISP programs.

4.3 GOALS AND META-GOALS

Many features of learning and of the evolution of living systems can be explained by postulating what may be termed *meta-goals* (Andrew 1979). By this is meant goals whose achievement brings no immediate material advantage to the organism, but facilitates the achievemnt of other, subsequent goals. Lenat (1984) has used the term *meta-heuristic* similarly, particularly to denote heuristics that operate to form other new heuristics. He observes that it is not useful to make any sharp distinction between meta-heuristics and domain heuristics.

Curiosity can be seen as the implementation of the meta-goal 'Collect information even if it is of no immediate value, since it may be useful later'. Skill acquisition in manual tasks depends on a meta-goal which says, 'Besides acting to achieve the immediate goal implicit in the task, make notes that will be useful if you ever want to pursue a similar goal again'.

Any reference to *goals* is a descriptive expedient which has to be justified. An explanation depending on such reference is automatically *teleological* since it explains events by reference to the future. According to some viewpoints teleological explanations are unacceptable, and in the early days of Cybernetics the main conflict between the new way of thinking and established methods in neurophysiology was the emphasis of the former on teleological arguments. It was wise to eliminate any trace of teleological explanation if a paper was intended, for example, for the *Journal of Physiology*.

In many contexts, including those of everyday living, teleological explanations seem to be entirely appropriate. A person who steps out of the path of an approaching motor car will say that the reason for the action is "Because it would have hit me if I had stayed where I was". This is an explanation that usually satisfies listeners, but for those who insist on avoiding teleology it can be replaced by a clumsy alternative that refers to the evolutionary and environmental origins of the neural capacity to extrapolate motion and to recognize certain features of the situation that trigger the initiation of a particular pattern of motor activity, and so on.

The place of teleological explanations has been argued at length in numerous works (Sommerhoff 1950, 1974; Maturana 1975; Weir 1984; Rosen 1985;

George and Johnson 1985; Andrew 1987d). In discussing intelligent behaviour it is almost impossible to avoid reference to goals, but it has to be kept in mind that this is essentially a descriptive expedient implying the existence of a tedious non-teleological explanation as outlined above. There is, however, an intangible sense in which the teleological explanation is more than merely a shorthand notation. As emphasized by Rosen, the full explanation 'misses the point' in much the same way as a description of a book as black marks on paper is undoubtedly valid, but 'misses the point' if the reason for interest is to explain, for example, why perusal of the book arouses a particular emotional response in a reader.

The ramifications of the argument can be taken further, and a set of philosophical comments has been assembled by George and Johnson (1985). Strictly, the reference above to a non-teleological explanation is not entirely defensible because our current state of knowledge of evolutionary and neural mechanisms does not let us develop this explanation in detail. In everyday living it is certainly not the basis of our confidence that a person with normal vision, intelligence and agility will step out of the path of an oncoming car if he is looking in the right direction. (There is, of course, more than a hint of tautology here, since we would brand anyone who did not step aside as not 'normal'.) The confidence stems from inductive inference based on an empirical internal model of human behaviour, within which teleological explanation is a valuable heuristic principle. This, however, does not exempt the teleological viewpoint from the challenge of the non-teleological alternative, since the establishment of the empirical internal model, heuristics and all, presumably has a neural basis; the teleological explanation is subsumed in the non-teleological one.

With this clarification (or obfuscation) of the meaning of a goal, it seems reasonable to view evolutionary development as being guided by meta-goals of extreme generality. The same idea has been advanced by Lenat (1984), expressed in terms of heuristics rather than goals, and his heuristic rule directing attention to extreme cases was discussed in section 3.6. The goal, or heuristic, of concise representation is not explicitly listed by Lenat but it is implicit in his ways of forming new heuristics.

In Lenat's AM program, new heuristics are given a rating of *worth* or *interestingness*, and some corresponding estimate clearly guides human work on mathematics and the evaluation of new findings as worthy of publication, etc. In accordance with the earlier remarks (Gaines 1977) about the estimated usefulness of models, the worth rating for heuristics could also appropriately include a *conciseness* term.

Although he speculates about its wider implications, the theories advanced by Lenat are associated with his experimental studies of automated mathematical discovery. This means that, right from the start, he is concerned with discrete concepts. On the other hand, as he acknowledges in his general discussion, the general or 'weak' heuristics he has discerned have origins that pre-date the use of spoken language.

It seems useful to carry the general approach to an early stage of evolutionary development and to consider the origin of the tendency to operate in terms of discrete concepts. This is the idea behind the reference to the *concept of a concept*. As already emphasized by reference to the behaviour of earthworms and to frog vision, the origins of this tendency certainly predate the use of spoken language (probably by many millions of years).

4.3.1 Persistence in Evolution

A characteristic of biological evolution is that it never quite forgets its past. The evolutionary history of the human species is re-enacted in foetal devlopment. Anatomists are fond of referring to parts of the physical structure of the brain as phylogenetically older than others. If structure is carried over from earlier forms, it is likely that function is also.

It should, however, be noted that function and structure need not be in one-to-one correspondence. Fulton (1949), for example, refers to the increasing *encephalization* of function with evolutionary development in primates, and a similar shift of function is seen by comparing the amphibian visual system with that of mammals. The much-quoted work on the frog visual system (Andrew 1955; Lettvin *et al* 1959; Gaze 1970) is qualitatively different from the studies on mammals initiated by Hubel and Wiesel (1962, 1968). Both sets of experiments are addressed to the main regions of the brain for visual processing in the respective species, but the regions do not correspond. The *optic lobes* of the frog brain correspond anatomically to the *superior colliculi* of the mammalian one, but in mammals the main site of visual processing has moved to the visual cortex. However, the *superior colliculi* in mammals are still involved in vision (Apter 1945; Hamdi and Whitteridge 1953), and the very fact that comparisons between species can be made in this way shows that new evolutionary developments are very far from starting from a *tabula rasa*.

The implication for the mechanism of inteLigence is that we should expect to find relics of more primitive information-processing systems playing a part in brain fuction. In particular there are likely to be relics of earlier systems that were much more directly concerned with the processing of continuous information. Although anatomists and physiologists recognize the importance of the evolutionary viewpoint, it tends to be neglected in connection with AI. If AI is to utilize principles derived from biological prototypes, the evolutionary nature of these has to be recognized.

The lesson for AI resarch is that discrete 'logic' should not be adopted as the starting-point. Instead, continuous processing should be seen as fundamental and the question to be considered is how a tendency to operate in terms of discrete concepts has emerged from it, or at least in conjunction with it. We do not have to consider how the continuous criteria of *heuristic connection* and *fuzzy set membership* can be imposed on a discrete framework since the evolutionary view suggests that continuous processing is a primitive capability.

The principle of *elementary exemplification* (Andrew 1977) mentioned in section 1.9, is a recognition that an 'elementary' or continuous thought process often parallels an 'advanced' or concept-based one. Minsky's reference to *heuristic connection* acknowledges a tendency to think about advanced problem-solving in terms of continuity similar to that exploited in bicycle-riding and other manipulative skills (Minsky 1969b, 1963). The idea behind the *basic learning heuristic* (Minsky and Selfridge 1961) is the same, and the reference to hill-climbing and its inadequacy when faced by the *mesa phenomenon* confirm the connection. (The mesa-phenomenon refers to the situation in hill-climbing where the operating point enters a region in which the gradient is zero in all directions so gives no guidance.)

Reference is often made to 'distance from a solution' in discussions of machine problem solving. People form some such estimate during their own problem-solving activity, and reference is sometimes made to the warm feeling of satisfaction that pervades the body as the solution is approached.

The means-ends analysis of Newell, Shaw and Simon (1959) requires the repeated asking of the question "What is the difference between what I have and what I want?" and then "What action would reduce the difference?". This has an elementary exemplification in servo, or negative-feedback, control. It is interesting that Wiener (1948) touches on this parallel in the introduction to his famous book.

Wiener refers to a person picking up a pencil from a desk and claims that the action can be seen as controlled by negative feedback. The indication of 'error' to be fed back has to be an estimate of the degree to which the task has not been accomplished. He discusses the problem as though the feedback signal could be expressed numerically, but in fact there is no numerical function that will serve the purpose. In practice the action has to be guided by something of the nature of means-ends analysis, perhaps with the setting-up of subgoals as in the general problem solver, or in the SHRDLU scheme (Winograd 1973; Hofstadter 1980) which is intended for problems of this sort. Wiener's comment illustrates the readiness with which people invoke a continuous *elementary exemplification*.

This readiness to invoke a parallel continuous problem presumably serves a purpose in human thinking. It is easy to feel that it holds a clue to an important respect in which the basis of human intelligence differs from that of the current machine kind; in fact the aim of this book is to advance this idea and to try to develop its implications. The way in which human thinking sometimes seems to be guided by an elementary exemplification is reminiscent of the attempt by Newell, Shaw and Simon to improve the operation of the general problem solver by introducing *planning*.

Newell, Shaw and Simon felt dissatisfied with the plodding, one-step-at-a-time, character of GPS operation, and tried to improve matters by letting it first form a skeleton of a proof to which it was to add 'flesh' later. In forming the skeleton proof it employed a reduced list of types of difference between the current and target expressions, and a reduced set of operators for transforming expressions. The idea was that in a second pass the GPS would use the skeleton as a guide in completing the proof, but the attempt at implementation of the two-pass scheme did not prove to be very successful. The scheme is, of course, an example of a general class of problem-solving methods designated by Minsky (1959a) as "methods which set up new problems as models".

At present it is certainly not possible to improve on the scheme by substituting a continuous *elementary exemplification* of the problem for the skeleton proof. Nevertheless, the fact that human thought readily has recourse to elementary exemplifications suggests that valuable insight can be gained by examining the evolutionary process by which the tendency to operate in terms of discrete concepts arose on the basis of mainly-continuous operation. Suggestions for its further study are made in the remainder of this chapter and in Chapter 5.

4.3.2 Remarks on Neural Coding

The idea that continuous variables are represented by density of excitation, whether spatial or temporal (section 3.2), is in general agreement with a comment by Anderson and Hinton (1981) on a difference between neural and electronic computation. They observe that, in neural processing, the representations are less abstract than in electronic computing, having internal structure that is in some sense an image of something in the real world. The structure plays a part in determining the effects and interactions.

An obvious way in which neural signals have such structure is seen when data having two-dimensional extension is conveyed. There are various examples of *mappings* which preserve neighbourhood relationships. The mappings that have received most attention from physiologists have been those associated with vision, but the body surface is also mapped in *homunculi* within the nervous system. The best-known of these are the *motor* and *sensory homunculi* of the human cerebral cortex, described in a great many texts on neuroanatomy and notably in Penfield and Rasmussen (1950). A similar sensory mapping at a lower level, in the rat brain, was the basis of experiments by Wall and Egger

(1971) which opened up a new area of investigation of neural plasticity.

Given this view of the functioning of the nervous system, it would be surprising if it did not process continuous variables in performing operations relevant to an external world which clearly has continuous aspects. On the other hand, it is possible to overstate the case, since the brain certainly operates at a certain level of abstraction even when performing everyday 'non-intellectual' tasks. On the sensory side it is well known that sensory data is pre-processed, in the visual cortex and elsewhere, in a way that would be appropriate at the beginning of a process of pattern classification and hence of representation in terms of discrete concepts. There is evidence for corresponding interface arrangements on the motor side; it has been found, for example, that electrical stimulation in the motor area of the cerebral cortex produces coordinated movements rather than contractions of the individual muscles (see, for example, Evans 1949).

However, it is easy to show that the simplistic view encouraged by references to pre-processing and interfacing is unrealistic. The visual system has to process data so as to allow recognition of classes of object, but for many purposes the recognition signal would be of little value if not accompanied by data on position, orientation, velocity, size, and other continuously-variable characteristics of the perceived object.

The danger of an over-simplistic view was illustrated by Jerry Lettvin in a lecture where he asked his audience to consider what is seen when a person looks at the sky on a clear night. The scatter of stars would be invisible if the person's visual system operated according to a naive interpretation of the results of Hubel and Wiesel. Their work suggests that a first stage in processing is the detection of edges, slits and bars in the visual field (since the *simple units* are usually interpreted as detectors of these features), but in the night sky, away from the periphery of the moon, there is not an edge, slit or bar anywhere.

This illustrates the complexity and versatility of neural processing , which led Fischler and Firschein (1987) to quote the remark of a colleague as:

"... if you think up any form of symbolism at all, it probably plays some role in thinking".

Even this is an understatement of the case; it would have been better if he had said 'representation' or 'coding' rather than 'symbolism' since the latter implies a bias towards discrete concepts and conventional logic.

On the motor, or effector, side of neural processing, there is evidence for some specialization of function, since the details of posture and muscular movement are worked out in the cerebellum, and internal regulation is the concern of the anatomically distinguishable parts of the system denoted as the *autonomic* nervous system. Here, too, it is easy to show that the compartmentalization of function is a loose one. If a person sits in an armchair and thinks about strenuous exercise (running a hundred metres, say), his heart and respiration rates increase as though in preparation. This shows that autonomic regulation is not simply a matter of feedback from internal sensors, but has links with conscious thought.

The cerebellum is an outgrowth from the brain stem, physically separated from the rest of the brain by a barrier which is a membrane in humans but a web of bone in other species. The function of the cerebellum is generally agreed to be to orchestrate motor activity, having regard to balance and posture as well as the dictates of the cerebral cortex. It is easy to underestimate the complexity of this task, and the need for it to have an adaptive or 'learning' character.

That the cerebellum should be viewed as something other than a simple interface device is emphasized by the theoretical treatments of Marr (1969) and Kanerva (1988). Both of these workers proposed theories of learning, and both were able to support their theories by reference to the fine anatomical structure of the cerebellum. This is partly because the cerebellar cortex has a particularly regular structure which lends itself to theoretical treatment. These workers claimed that their theories were also applicable to other parts of the central nervous system (Marr 1970, 1971). In these other regions the theory is less easily related to the anatomical structure because the latter is more haphazard.

The fine anatomy of the cerebellar cortex has a regular structure reminiscent of an associative net or *lernmatrix* (Steinbuch ad Piske 1963). The anatomical terminology acknowledges this in its use of the terms *climbing fibre* and *parallel fibre*. Kanerva briefly describes the anatomy and a short excerpt illustrates the lernmatrix-like character:

> "The *Purkinje cells* are aligned, almost in rows, perpendicular to the parallel fibers. The broad and flat dendrite systems of a row form a plane perpendicular to the parallel fibers. The dendrite planes are stacked side by side like books on a shelf, and a single parallel fiber passes through many (200–450) such planes, forming synapses with some if not all of them (estimates range from 45 to 450). The arrangement is ideal for bringing many parallel fibers into contact with many Purkinje cells ... ".

Although this part of the nervous system is concerned with motor control and posture, it has structure and compellingly suggests a mechanism for conceptual learning. This emphasizes the complex relationship of continuous and concept-based processing.

4.4 THE EMERGENCE OF CONCEPTS

The origins of life are shrouded in mystery, and may have been extra-terrestrial (Hoyle and Wickramasinghe 1980). It seems safe to assume that the first organisms were unicellular and had little if any motility. It has been shown (Bellman and Goldberg 1984) that the behaviour of some unicellular organisms is quite complex, but the first to appear were presumably relatively simple and essentially vegetative. Even the description as *vegetative* does not necessarily imply the absence of behaviour best described in terms of concepts. A great deal of country lore suggests that plants are able to benefit from their own internal weather-forecasting arrangements, and are better able to recognize the significant patterns in environmental conditions than are most humans.

The simplest imaginable concept that could be of use to a simple organism would be the recognition of a particular level (high, medium, low) of concentration of a noxious or nutritive substance or of the rate of change of a concentration. It is easy to imagine that recognition of such a concept (indicating 'dangerous environment') could be useful in triggerins a discrete action such as sealing-off all channels of absorption. If there was then a set of conditions that caused them to be opened up again, recognition of it could be said to correspond to the concept of 'safe environment'. Kochen (1981) remarks that:

"Edibility was probably one of the earliest concepts that was formed".

The general idea is perhaps most readily illustrated by thinking of creatures swimming in a medium that has an uneven distribution of noxious and nutrient substances. Some such creatures can be seen to make tail-flicks at irregular intervals, resulting in an apparently random re-assignment of the direction of travel. I am indebted to Andrew Barto for describing this behaviour in an informal discussion of the work on learning reported in Barto, Sutton and Brouwer (1980).

If the tail-flicks are to be useful to the animals, they should be triggered when either the concentration of a nutrient substance is falling, or that of a noxious substance is rising, while the animal follows its current direction of travel. Possibly the various concentrations would be combined in an estimate of a 'comfort level' or 'survivability level' (like Wiener's *affective tone* or Selfridge's *hedony*), and a tail-flick would be appropriate if the value of this estimate was falling significantly.

It is likely that concept-based behaviour originated with some simple example such as this. It was not only pre-linguistic, but prior even to the appearance of nervous systems. At a much later stage of evolution it was vastly elaborated in the brains, particularly the cerebral cortices, of the higher mammals.

In initiating tail-flicks as described, the swimming organisms are effectively implementing a stochastic hill-climbing algorithm, the altitude of the hill being the comfort level or hedony. The hill grows out of the three-dimensional territory in which an organism's location is represented, so there are four dimensions in all.

It is interesting that one of the best-known methods for automatic optimization by hill-climbing (Rosenbrock 1960; Schwefel 1981; Andrew 1985) embodies a mechanism for periodic revision of the principal direction of advance. There are various differences between the computer-optimization and swimming-organism situations, but they agree in indicating that discrete events can play a part in continuous optimization. Once it is acknowledged that the discrete events of direction-change can play a part, it follows that it is useful to recognize a concept that can be described as 'appropriateness of a direction-change'.

One of the differences between the computer-optimization situation and that of the swimming organism is that Rosenbrock's operating point can 'swim' either backwards or forwards along the assigned direction. Associated with this is a different criterion for triggering the direction-change. Two further differences are that Rosenbrock's method makes explorations in directions orthogonal to the main one, and the new principal direction adopted at each reassignment is not selected randomly. Instead it is aligned with the overall advance of the operating point since the previous direction-assignment. In the terminology of modern computing, the Rosenbrock method makes 'smart' tail-flicks.

In spite of these rather major points of difference there is more than a superficial correspondence between the tail-flicks of swimming organisms and the direction-reassignments of Rosenbrock's method. The task environments are essentially similar and it would be surprising if the apparent similarity of solution was fortuitous.

Lovelock's 'parable' of *Daisyworld* (section 2.12) shows how a regulatory function can arise as a feature of a simple ecological system. It is most readily associated with an evolutionary stage at which some life forms are capable of independent existence and replication. Prior to this stage, life forms presumabley evolved their own internal mechanisms of regulation. It is tempting to try to extend the parable to account for the origin of this internal regulation.

The idea of black and white daisies can be generalized to include anything that proliferates at a rate which is a single-peaked function of an environmental variable and satisfies some other simple conditions. One condition is that there are at least two varieties of the proliferating agent and that the varieties influence the environmental variable differently. It is necessary that at least two of the varieties have influences of opposing sign. The effect on the environmental variable must be mainly local, but with global spread, and of course the proliferation process must have a 'like begets like' character.

Cell physiologists may be able to identify suitable proliferating agents to satisfy the conditions of this model. It could only refer to the very early appearance of internal regulation. Environmental pressures would ensure that a species improving on this primitive mechanism would greatly enhance its own viability, and so the evolution of complex regulatory methods would commence. The introduction of discrete responses (e.g. tail-flicks), and hence of concepts, would be one such improvement.

4.4.1 Evolution of Communication

Consideration of the nature of internal communication in living systems shows a curious alternation of the continuous and the discrete (Andrew 1982).

Primitive living systems are much concerned with the processing of continuous information. However, the genetic code, on which they also depend, seems to be essentially discrete, having a rough analogy wih punched paper tape.

In multi-cellular organisms a number of special subsystems for communication were evolved, the one that has proved most interesting, in the light of subsequent developoments, being the nervous system. The main means of communication in the nervous system is the propogated impulse resulting from the all-or-nothing excitation of a neuron. An all-or-nothing event is ideally suited to convey conceptual information, and in relatively primitive animals the firing of one, or a very few, neurons can represent an event in the external world and trigger a response of the organism. Many species of worm, for example, have *giant axons* running the length of the animal and producing a 'startle' or 'escape' response. (The giant axon of the squid has reiieved a great deal of attention because it is big enough to allow experiments that would otherwise be hardly feasible, in which electrodes are placed within the axon itself. Much of our understanding of the detailed mechanism of nervous transmission comes from such experiments.)

In higher animals, however, as discussed in section 3.1, nerve cells seem to operate in a manner more suited to the transmission of continuous than discrete information. This seems a curious direction of development since the later development of the nervous system is towards greater dependence on discrete concepts. Presumably the anomaly is related to the fact that the primitive animals (worms, squid, sea anemones) respond to a limited set of concepts, and these are determined genetically. The higher aimals are able to learn new concepts, and processing of sensory data is such that commitment to a specific set of concepts is delayed as long as possible. This is in accordance with the principle of *least commitment* due to Marr (1976, 1982).

Obviously, the higher animals *do* operate in terms of concepts, so digital yes/no responses must occur somewhere in the brain. It is usually assumed that the seat of the 'higher' mental processes is the cerebral cortex, and concepts seem to be associated with special structures there. A number of theoretical treatments, including those of Wilson and Cowan (1972), Harth *et al* (1970) and Fish (1981) suggest that an all-or-nothing , or *bistable flipflop* effect results from the combination of groups of neurons into *cell assemblies* with internal positive feedback. The term *cell assembly* is originally due to Hebb (1961, 1980).

It is instructive to recapitulate the alternation of discrete and continuous aspects in the evolution of biological information processing. The information processing of primitive creatures must have been mainly continuous as far as chemical and metabolic regulation was concerned. On the other hand the genetic code was an early development having discrete character. In very primitive nervous systems, discrete operation is fairly common, with the all-or-nothing feature of neural transmission apparent in the overall behaviour of the animal. More advanced nervous systems largely disguise the all-or-nothing character by using neurons in such a way that they are effectively continuous elements. Then, rather incredibly, in the higher centres of these more advanced nervous systems, the continuous channels double back on themselves so as to produce bi-stable flip-flops that again have all-or-nothing character.

The situation is a little more complicated because neural structures having a set of discrete stable states are not restricted to the cerebral cortex. The *reticular formation* is a phylogenetically-ancient structure, constituting the core of the spinal cord. In humans and other higher animals it becomes thicker in the lower spinal region, and in humans it also bulges considerably in the neck and brain stem. It can be identified in all vertebrate nervous systems; at the millipede level of evolution it constitutes the entire central nervous system. Even in humans,it still acts to coordinate the activity of all other subdivisions of the central nervous system which can in fact be regarded as appendages to enhance its function (Kilmer, McCulloch and Blum 1968, 1969; Delgado, Mira and Moreno-Diaz, 1989). In an earlier report, McCulloch says of the problem of understanding the reticular formation:

> "By comparison with this problem all other neurophysiological problems seem truly parochial."

The reticular formation commits the animal to one of a number of discrete modes of behaviour. Examples of modes are sleep, eat, drink, fight, flee and mate. It is claimed there are never more than about 25 such modes for any given animal, and if properly interpreted they are mutually exclusive. The need for 'proper interpretation' is illustrated by observing that urination can be regarded as a mode, but the fact that animals often urinate while fleeing does not mean that urination and flight modes can co-exist. The fleeing animal has all its attention firmly focussed on escape, so its nervous system is in the flight mode and the act of urination is incidental.

In the higher animals the reticular formation has links with all other parts of the central nervous system, and integrates a great deal of sensory information as the basis for its mode selection. Kilmer, McCulloch and Blum claim that a mode-change in this complex structure, containing about two million neurons in the human, can occur in a fraction of a second. The already-mentioned ability of the visual system to perform complex recognition tasks (Marr 1982; Sejnowski 1986) in a short space of time is also displayed in the phylogenetically older reticular formation. The development of the latter, in the first vertebrates, was an important stage in the evolution of the ability to use discrete concepts at the pre-linguistic level.

The information-processing capability of the human brain has been enhanced by developments that are cultural and technological rather than neural. The development of spoken language seems to have been partly cultural and partly neural, since there are areas of the brain dedicated to it. The subsequent invention of written language gave the possibility of externalized memory, which then allowed the development of mathematics. It is possible to think of forms of externalized memory that do not depend on writing, or even on language (in the everyday sense), but a great advance came with writing and the invention of number systems.

These developments obviously depend on concept-based processing, but continuity is also important, as illustrated by the remarks on language in section 3.6. The ultimate (so far) external enhancement to human thought is the digital computer. Since it depends on binary digits and hence on 'logical' (in sense A) operations, it can be seen as the total vindication of concept-based processing, until it is realised that many of the facilities traditionally provided in a digital computer are devised with a very strong awareness of continuity. The introduction of number systems, especially the Arabic one as enhanced by Napier's invention of the decimal point, is a way of combining continuity (in the large) with the precision and reproducibility of digital methods.

It can be seen that, from the origins of biological information processing to its most recent external enhancements, there is a curious interplay and alternation of representations that are apparently discrete with others that are essentially continuous. The many arguments in this book show that continuous aspects are more pervasive than is generally thought.

5

Continuous Heuristics

5.1 THE ARGUMENT

The overall argument of the book is that attempts to understand and to model intelligent behaviour are fundamentally limited by their failure to take proper account of continuity. This is certainly not to deny that extremely important advances have been made—the AI approach is not erroneous, merely blinkered. In particular, the assertion that thought processes are guided by *heuristics* seems indisputable and represents a valuable insight.

The subtle ways in which continuity enters into intelligence have been portrayed here as an evolutionary carry-over from more primitive systems. The primitive systems also survive to serve their original purposes, since humans still need regulation of the *milieu intérieur*, as well as feedback control of muscular action.

The achievements of AI have been in areas where the continuous aspects of processing can be largely ignored, or partitioned from the 'logical' (in sense A of Chapter 1) aspects. The writer has argued (Andrew 1884, 1987a,c) that the needs of robotics will prompt a departure from this restriction that will eventually alter the character of AI itself. This is in accordance with the view, attributed to Sherrington, that all thinking should be regarded as a development of motor control. The needs of robotics should encourage AI to emulate this biological development.

A step in the required direction can be made by extending the idea of a *heuristic* to take account of continuity. Ideas for doing this in the robotics context are presented in this chapter, along with some experimental findings.

5.1.1 Minsky's Argument

The writer's original development of the above viewpoint was much influenced by Minsky's idea of *heuristic connection* (Minsky 1959b, 1963; Andrew 1980). It was therefore surprising to find that Marvin Minsky is quoted by McCorduck (1979) as expressing a view of the place of robotics that is diametrically opposed to the one given here. His conclusions are so precisely opposed that quoting them is a good way of clarifying both sides of the argument.

McCorduck herself seems mildly surprised at his "lukewarm stand on robotics as a way of doing AI". She quotes him as saying:

> "You might say that robotics was a kind of hobby which I encouraged but didn't really concern myself with that much, and I always felt that studying the sensory and perceptual systems is not the best way to think about thinking, because the sensory systems are developed in lower animals as well, and come prior to symbolic intelligence. So you can study those things to death and you may only learn about some hardware tricks that were developed over a few million years that don't really tell you how the problem-solving parts of the brain work."

He goes on to say that, although it may have looked, from the outside, as though the Artificial Intelligence Laboratory of M.I.T. was doing a great deal of work on robotics, this was not the area to which he gave particular attention. He refers to the thesis work of three well-known researchers as typifying what he sees as the most profitable approach.

The three references are to Slagle (1963) on symbolic integration and to Bobrow (1968) and Raphael (1968) on question-answering and problem-solving systems using natural language.

5.1.2 Other Arguments

Of course, in a many-faceted subject such as this, it is perhaps unfair to place so much emphasis on Marvin Minsky's remarks in one particular discussion. On the other hand, his viewpoint should be considered very seriously since it is the outcome of a long period of involvement in these matters, with exposure to conflicting approaches. At an early stage, influenced by McCulloch, he concerned himself with neural net models (see Minsky 1976), and it was following a lead given by him that I learned of the work of his colleagues Paynter (1960) and Philbrick (1960) referred to in section 2.11.5.

However, the viewpoint as quoted is an extreme example of the 'assumption', popular among philosophers, that the brain processes that make for cognition are one sort of thing and that the brain processes that contribute to motor control belong to an entirely different category", as contested by Churchland

(1986). It would be surprising if neural evolution made a totally fresh start with the advent of symbolic reasoning.

McCorduck is also able to quote a remark by von Neumann to the effect that:

> "The human nervous system also shows clear signs of both discrete and continuous behaviour, whereas computers must be either discrete (digital) or continuous (analog)."

Von Neumann was of course aware that continuous behaviour can be simulated digitally, but his comment underlines the fact that continuity is inherent in analog computation in a way that is not true of the digital kind. It also shows that he felt there was a real problem in understanding how the brain combines the two. It is worth noting that interest in analog computing methods is by no means dead, and in a recent paper Roska (1988) describes a dual computing structure with interesting capabilities. This can execute some complex algorithms in a very much shorter time than would be needed with purely digital operation. Roska argues that his hybrid system is a useful model of information-processing in the brain, and reviews neurological evidence bearing on this, with particular attention to the respective roles of the two cerebral hemispheres.

5.2 A SPEEDING-UP ROBOT

Most existing robotic devices do in fact separate the function of motion planning (or, for simpler devices, simply memory of required movements) from that of turning the commands into physical movements. The latter has to depend on stiff servo-mechanisms, and the resulting robots are correspondingly slower in operation, and less energetically efficient, then they need be. One reason is that the movements are likely to be precisely regulated to a prescribed path even in parts of the trajectory where such precision is unnecessary.

People and animals develop skill in tasks as they repeat them. For many manipulative tasks the main result of practice is an increase in speed, and it would certainly be useful if industrial robots were able to emulate this form of skill acquisition. Unless the actuator arms are stiff under all the conditions of load and speed that can be achieved, an increase in speed, without modification of the pattern of input control will cause departures from the low-speed trajectory because of inertia. The system must be capable of detecting these departures and deciding whether they, and the forces arising, are acceptable. Unduly large forces could damage the robot itself, or its workpiece, and could result in damage to other objects in the vicinity if the workpiece or a tool broke loose.

A robot learning to go faster must embody a characteristic that plays a part in human learning, in that it must be aware of 'near misses'. A person learning a complex and potentially hazardous skill, like driving a car, normally learns a great deal by noting situations in which an accident could have occurred, even though nothing untoward actually happened. The learning process has to be influenced, not only by feedback of a low value of hedony because of an unpleasant material outome, but by such feedback supplemented by a facility for extrapolation, or 'imagination'.

For a robot performing a simple manipulative task the required avoidance of 'near misses' could be achieved simply by storing a representation of the boundaries of obstacles as though they extended further, by some margin, than their true physical limits. Then a violation of this extended boundary should have much the same effect on the learning process as would a true collision. Similarly, a margin of safety can be associated with limits set for forces.

Of course, in complex situations where some of the obstacles may also be moving, the recognition of 'near miss' situations is not so easily achieved. For the present purpose attention can be restricted to the simpler situation and it will be assumed that an acceptable trajectory must remian within a specified three-dimensional envelope. It will also be assumed, as a gross over-simplification of the practical case, that there is only one point whose trajectory need be considered. (Obviously, for a robot or human arm, trajectories have to be planned so that no part of the arm, nor of what it is carrying, collides with anything else.)

It is possible to visualize a type of robot that initially discovers, or is shown, how to carry out a task slowly, and then starts to speed-up the action. It starts with what may be termed, by analogy with the terminology of linear programming, a *feasible trajectory*, i.e. one that leads from a specified initial state to a goal state without violating the constraints.

To begin, the robot might discover a feasible trajectory by some process of random or systematic exploration, which might be referred to as physically groping towards a solution. If the geometry of the obstacles has been totally mapped out it may be possible to derive the minimum-distance feasible trajectory. Where the envelopes of obstacles are represented as polyhedra the minimum-distance path must consist of a succession of straight-line segments meeting on polyhedral edges. Alternatively, in the industrial context, the robot might be 'trained' by being taken slowly over a feasible trajectory under manual control. Such 'training' is a usual way of setting-up industrial robots.

5.2.1 Robot Path Control

Techniques for planning the movements of robot manipulators are currently receiving a great deal of attention. Where the requirement is to trace a single-line trajectory, optimized according to some stated criterion, and subject to known constraints, a mathematical technique that may be applicable is well known under the heading of *calculus of variations* (see, for example Craggs 1963; Wylie and

Barrett 1982). The classical problem for which the method was devised is that of the *brachistochrone.* This was solved by the Bernoulli brothers, and the requirement is to find the time-optimal trajectory for a small bead, starting from rest and sliding under gravity on a frictionless wire from a given point in space to another at a lower altitude.

In general the finishing point is not directly beneath the starting point, and the problem is to decide how the wire should be shaped in order to minimize the transit time of the bead. A straight wire minimizes the distance travelled, but if it is formed into a curve that is concave upward the bead accelerates more rapidly in the early part of the trajectory, and it is worth while to accept some extra distance in order to gain the advantage this gives in average speed. It has been shown to be optimal to let the curve be part of a cycloid.

The *brachistochrone* problem is particularly amenable since the only constraints are the *boundary conditions,* i.e. the coordinates of the starting and finishing points. In more complex situations, additional constraints can often be taken into account, provided they are represented by equations that are differentiable with respect to the independent variables. However, in practical problems of optimal control, constraints often arise that cannot be represented in this way; constraints ensuring collision avoidance are examples.

Extensions of the *calculus of variations* approach, so as to allow inequality constraints, have been developed under two main headings. One is due to Pontryagin *et al* (1963), and another depends on *dynamic programming* (Bellman 1961). The two are contrasted in a useful introductory text by Craggs (1963) as well as in other standard works.

Provided the dynamics and constraints are fully represented, these mathematical methods often allow the derivation of optimal trajectories. The computational complexity may, however, be such that the methods are not suitable for on-line robot control. The problem of finding minimum-time paths, or paths approximating the minimum-time condition, has been studied by Troch (1989a, b). He has devised computational techniques suitable for on-line use.

Needless to say, other complications can arise in practical robotics. Obstacles to be avoided need not be stationary, and in other ways the constraints and dynamics may not be fully known before the movement begins. Principles of adaptive control to allow for variations in the dynamics are dicussed by Warwick and Pugh (1988). The specification of a movement path is normally more complicated than the derivation of a single-line trajectory, since it is necessary that no part of the robot arm or its workpiece collides with anything. The computational difficulties associated with the *sofa problem* (sometimes called the *piano-mover's problem*) are well known, and complex problems of this sort arise in robotics.

The complexity of the necessary on-line calculations is increased by the need to translate, in both directions, between 'world coordinates', usually Cartesian, and the 'joint coordinates' of the robot device. Attention has been given to the problem of allowing, within this, for flexibility of the robot structure.

5.2.2 Geometric Reasoning

Special difficulties arise when computers are applied to geometrical problems. Some of them are apparent in connection with the *sofa problem*, or *piano-mover's problem*, mentioned earlier; this is the problem of deciding whether (and if so, how) a two-dimensional shape can be moved past a set of obstructions. The techniques of mathematical theorem-proving by computer are usually explored and illustrated with reference to algebra and formal logic, which lend themselves to digital representation more readily than does geometry. Theorem-proving in geometry has received attention since quite early in the history of AI but has proved more difficult.

Computational techniques for dealing with geometric reasoning are treated in a book edited by Kapur and Mundy (1989). The special difficulties are particularly interesting because they indicate a significant mismatch between human and machine capabilities. For example, the writing of computer programs to play the game of *Go* has proved to be more difficult than that of writing powerful chess-playing ones, and the difference has been attributed (Good 1965) to the fact that the specification of the goal in *Go* is essentially geometric or topological. The goal is to surround 'islands' on the board filled with the opponent's pieces, by areas filled with the player's own pieces. Humans have a special aptitude for dealing with geometrical aspects in a way that is not currently imitated by artifacts.

5.2.3 Motion Heuristics

Kapur and Mundy review, in their Introduction, mathematical developments that allow a significant improvement in the geometric reasoning that can be realized by computer programs. The developments are further elaborated in papers reproduced in the volume, and that of Schwartz and Sharir (1989) surveys algorithms having a bearing on motion planning.

These papers present rigorous, analytic methods, which certainly do not correspond to the processes underlying human and animal motor control. The latter are empirical and justified by the fact that they usually 'work'. They have the same character as the *heuristic* rules employed in other areas of AI, with the difference that continuity is now apparent.

The complexity and non-robustness of rigorous methods has prompted some workers in robotics to consider other possibilities. One effective method of motion control is based on a hypothetical potential field in the space to be traversed (Khatib 1986; Freund and Hoyer 1988). Potentials are computed as though the desired end-point of the trajectory is charged so as to attract the manipulator, and obstcles to be avoided are charged so as to repel it. A smooth collision-free trajectory is obtained by letting the movement be aligned with the potential gradient throughout.

The method has many attractive features. It has been described above with reference to a single-line trajectory, but in fact a number of points on the same robot may be considered simultaneously in order to determine complex movements. Khatib uses the term *PSP* to denote *Point Subjected to the Potential*. Variations of the method can be used for preliminary movement planning and also for low-level on-line control. In the latter role the method has the important advantage that the computed potential field can be altered during the movement to take account of new information from sensors. This allows collision avoidance when some of the obstacles are able to move (provided they do not move too quickly). The mobile obstacles could be other robots.

Although the basis of the method is the computation of potentials, it is not necessary for these to correpond exactly to the electrical potentials that would exist if the objects near the path were in fact electrically charged as postulated. Khatib's 'field theory' is not that of physical electrostatics; it is devised to be computationally convenient and has been found to serve his purpose. In the version advocated in his 1986 paper, the influenc of a 'charged' body extends for a finite distance, the distance being in fact a parameter of the method and chosen with regard to manipulator dynamics.

Although the potential-field approach provides effective algorithms for pratical robot control, its basis is essentially heuristic. It gives no guarantee of finding a path that is optimal for transit time or any other criterion. On the other hand, the smooth trajectories it traces are probably not far removed from those that are optimal according to the main criteria that might be considered in practice. The smoothness of the paths implies the absence of large accelerations, and hence economy of actuator energy and a saving of wear and tear of the robot mechanism.

Unless some other approach supersedes it, the method will presumably be gradually improved in detail, on the basis of comparative trials of alternative versions as applied to route-finding through particularly awkward configurations of obstacles. This is similar to the development of heuristic rules in, for example, theorem-proving, where alternative heuristic strategies are compared according to the efficiency with which the programs embodying them are able to discover proofs of particular theorems.

Although the title *Continuous Heuristics* is meant to be mildly provocative, most definitions of a *heuristic* do not exclude continuity. A heuristic is often equated with a 'rule of thumb', and this term suggests a method used by a carpenter or other artisan to attach a suitable value to a linear dimension.

The various methods for automatic optimization, such as that of Rosenbrock (1960), are essentially heuristic procedures operating in a continuous environment. Rosenbrock's method is quite elaborate, and like other heuristic strategies it is the outcome of a long period of empirical development. It is an example of a hill-climbing method, and it has been found that such methods often halt, or become very slow, while the operating point is still some way from the summit or optimum. This tends to happen when the approach to the summit is along a gently-rising, steep-sided ridge, especially if it is a curved ridge.

Where the optimization is with respect to more than two independent variables, the hill and its ridge exist in a space of more than three dimensions so cannot readily be visualized. The shape of the hill is, of course, a representation of the function to be optimized, and Rosenbrock gives examples of functions that are particularly intractable because of sharp curving ridges in their mapping in hyperspace. His method, as descibed, was found to be better able to proceed along these ridges than any other he tried. However, it is not always successful, and various enhancements introduced by later workers are reviewed by Box (1965).

Any of these methods can be applied to the optimization of a physical system simulated within the computer program (or connected on-line through suitable transducers, though this is generally less convenient). The simulation must be such that the outcome, or objective function, depends on a finite set of independent variables.

Rosenbrock's method repeatedly reorientates a set of orthogonal directions in the hyperspace, and the intention is that one of these should come to be aligned with the crest of any ridge to be traversed by the operating point. (Strictly, the set of orthogonal directions is in the n-dimensional space defined by the n independent variables, not the $(n + 1)$-dimensional space in which the hill exists.). The existence of a ridge indicates interaction between the independent variables, in respect of their effect on the objective function. Where the objective function is evaluated by simulating a physical system, the identification of a ridge may correspond to the recognition of a *heuristic* having relevance to effective control. This point will be illustrated later in a specific context.

In performing its reorientation in multi-dimensional space, the numerical optimization procedure may be said to model some aspects of intelligence. Only very simple heuristic principles can be 'discovered' in this way, and in the standard version of the method they are represented only transiently. Nevertheless is seems worth while to try to apply this general optimization method to a problem of the kind arising in the robotics context, at least as a first step before considering application-specific methods.

A preliminary study of the application of Rosenbrock's method to optimization of a trajectory is reported in the remainder of this chapter. An extra reason for interest in such an approach is the similarity between the reassignment of orthogonal directions and the tail-flicks of primitive swimming organisms. Appreciation of the conditions in which reorientating tail-flicks are desirable has been advanced as an early manifestation of the evolution of the 'concept of a concept' (Chapter 4).

5.2.4 Representations

It would be useful to be able to understand and imitate the heuristic strategies playing a part in human and animal motor control and many studies having a bearing on robotics are also relevant to neurophysiology. It is not easy to apply introspection to the principles involved in posture and everyday activities like walking, because these have become highly automatic. It is easier to be introspective about relatively artificial areas of activity such as driving a car. An experienced driver, assumed to be in a hurry, makes many complex decisions as he views the road ahead.

He may decide that he can negotiate a difficult section without slackening speed, provided his steering action is appropriate, or he may decide it is necessary to reduce speed before reaching the difficult part. If he chooses to slacken speed he has to take account of the properties of the car and the nature of the road surface in deciding how far in advance to begin doing so. He may decide that the difficult section is best negotiated by accelerating through it, to give the advantage of 'power oversteer', or if a very sharp turn is needed he may choose to provoke a rear-end skid in the manner familiar to watchers of car chases in television police dramas.

An attraction of the 'speeding-up robot' as an object of study is that it demands heuristic decisions under conditions having some correspondence to those faced by the car-driver. If the action is speeded-up until a constraint is violated (a recognized 'near miss' being equivalent, for this purpose, to an actual collision), then either the steering prior to the violation must be amended, or else the speed must be reduced over some appropriate segment of the trajectory. One strategy would be to attempt to correct the course by adjusting the steering, and to resort to speed reduction if this was unsuccessful. However, a heuristic rule for making the decision without trial runs is essential for the motorist and could greatly accelerate the convergence of the robot optimization.

As will be illustrated in the specific context of the experiments to be described, the steering adjustments need not be confined to the segment of path immediately preceding the point of violation.

The speed reduction would normally be done by applying deceleration, or easing-back on acceleration, over a portion of the trajectory preceding the point of violation. It is not easy to formulate a general rule to determine the section of prior trajectory over which the easing-back would be imposed, nor to make a guess at the amount of easing-back needed. It is also desirable to speed-up the movement beyond the point of violation, if the later part of the trajectory has been found to be negotiable at the original speed. (The situation is complicated by the fact that the critical part of the trajectory, where speed reduction can be beneficial, is probably not adjacent to the actual point of violation, but is more likely to be a section of strong curvature some way ahead of it—in car-driving terms, there is usually an interval between the loss of control on a bend and impact with a barrier.)

These considerations have been introduced in an imprecise way, and it is hoped that this gives an intuitive feeling for the task situation. Precisely what is changed when the robot is made to speed-up has not been made clear— the discussion has been as though there was some imprecise control like the accelerator pedal of a car. To be more precise about the robotics task it is necessary to specify various physical aspects more exactly. It is, for example, necessary to state whether the object moving along the trajectory is able to accelerate freely like an object in outer space, or is subject to frictional or viscous damping.

It is also necessary to know the constraints on the force available to influence the trajectory. There is presumably an upper limit to the magnitude of the applied force, but possibly none on the direction in which it is made to act. In practical robot actuators, as in human limbs, the available force is strongly dependent on position, but for simplicity this is ignored here.

It is easy to underestimate the difficulty of finding suitable heuristics. An initial problem is to decide how the control action should be represented in the robot's memory. Three fairly obvious possibilities are as follows:

(a) A record can be stored of the applied force (both magnitude and direction) over the trajectory. In practice the record would take the form of a sequence of stored values corresponding to equal increments of some suitable variable. The x-coordinate would be a suitable independent variable if the trajectory lies substantially parallel to the x-axis. The choice of a suitable independent variable may not be a simple matter; neither elapsed time nor path-length along the trajectory itself would be satisfactory when the trajectory is subject to change. This is because the locations of obstacles, and of the goal-point, are not fixed in terms of these variables.

(b) A record can be kept of a *paradigm trajectory*, stored as a sequence of coordinate values defining points along it, as well as a time value for each point. Then the robot action would be produced by letting an imaginary *target point* follow the paradigm trajectory at a rate determined by the stored time values. The robot manipulator would be propelled by a force acting along a line from its actual position to the target point, roughly as though it was joined to the latter by a piece of elastic. That is to say, the manipulator would be servoed on to the target point. The magnitude of the force would be a non-decreasing function of the separation of these two points, possibly with a derivative component to damp possible oscillation, and bounded above by the assumed upper limit on the force the robot is able to achieve.

(c) A variation on (b) would be to store the coordinates of a set of *way points*, much smaller in number than the data points along the paradigm trajectory. Initially the manipulator would be propelled in the direction of a line joining it to the first way point, and when this could be said to have been 'reached' it would be propelled towards the second way point, and so on. To allow variation in speed it would be necessary to store, for every way point, a strength of attraction determining the magnitude of the force applied during its period of effectiveness.

In a real-world situation in which the robot may be subject to unpredictable disturbances and deviations from assumptions (e.g. regarding the mass of a load to be moved, or amount of friction), methods (b) and (c) are more robust than (a) since they embody servo control.

The operation of (c) requires the definition of a suitable criterion for deciding that a way point has been 'reached', so that the next one in the sequence becomes the effective target. This is quite a difficult problem, since the intention is that the manipulator should move ballistically and as the speed is increased its path diverges more and more from a straight line joining the way points. It would clearly be counter-productive if it circled round to converge on a particular way point it had passed, ignoring a clear path ahead to the next one. On the other hand there could be a danger in allowing the switch-over of target point too readily, since this would reduce the effectiveness of a way point in holding a portion of the trajectory clear of a projecting obstacle.

In making these slightly anthropomorphic comments on the operation of way point control no account has been taken of the fact that the intention is to embody the representation in a learning controller. Reference was made earlier to 'steering' the manipulator, and changes in steering action would be produced by altering the coordinates of the way points. The method of adjustment is part of the 'learning' capability of the robot and if this is sufficiently powerful the final trajectory may be substantially independent of small variations in the criterion adopted for deciding that a way point has been 'reached'.

However, the rate of convergence on the final trajectory may be affected by the choice of criterion, since convergence is fastest if the independent variables are orthogonal in their effects. Also, the robustness of the control achieved, with regard to unpredicatable disturbances or departures from assumptions, is certainly affected by the choice.

Where the trajectory is substantially parallel to one axis, say the x-axis, a way point can be assumed to have been 'reached' once its x-coordinate is exceeded by that of the manipulator. If the way points are evenly spaced in the x-direction, method (c) then approximates method (b), but extra complications arise if the way point coordinates are adjustable in the x-direction as well as in the y-direction. Again talking anthropomorphically, the way points must be prevented from clustering near the beginning of the trajectory to 'help out' if the manipulator has difficulty in negotiating an early obstacle. This could obviously be counter-productive for later adjustments. An alternative is to let the way points be introduced and removed according to suitable heuristic rules, like the *key points* discussed in section 2.11.5.

The representation method (c) has been considered in some detail because it seems to offer the possibility of defining the robot action in terms of relatively few parameters. However, for conceptual simplicity the experiments to be described use method (a). With computer simulation, the robustness of methods (b) and (c), with regard to unpredictable disturbances, is not immediately significant. There would, of course, have been an advantage in adopting one of these robust methods in order to inprove the relevance of the findings to practical robotics, but the increase in computational complexity of the simulation is formidable.

It is well known that biological motor control incorporates feedback from special receptors in muscles, joints and tendons, so presumably has some correspondence to method (b) or (c). On the other hand, very rapid and yet precise movements are made in typing and piano-playing, and it is hardly possible that these are servo-controlled, considering the relatively low conduction velocities of nerve fibres. It looks as though biological motor control is able to operate according to method (a) under some conditions, though perhaps only for types of activity for which a period of rehearsal or practice is possible prior to the critical performance.

There is still much to be learned about the representations underlying biological motor control. One way of investigating them is to ask a human subject to perform some continued movement, and to observe how an instruction to alter one parameter of the movement affects other parameters. Wallace (1989) asked subjects to make oscillatory movements of the forearm, and then to reduce the amplitude of oscillation. This was invariably accompanied by an increase in oscillation frequency. The electrical activity of the relevant muscles was recorded, and showed some variation in control strategy from subject to subject. Experiments such as this provide data against which proposed theories, about the representations underlying motor control, can be checked.

5.3 A RELEVANT EXPERIMENT

As in other areas of AI, the way to explore the nature of the heuristics involved in motor control is presumably to set up simplified problem situations, and to find techniques to solve them. Progress is of course critically dependent on an appropriate choice of 'toy problem'.

To explore the nature of heuristics playing a part in the operation of a speeding-up robot, it is interesting to consider the motion of a small object, having mass, past a set of obstacles such as that shown in Fig. 1. For simplicity, allowance is made for viscous damping, i.e. a retarding force proportional to velocity, but not for Coulomb friction. The object is assumed to have unit mass and to start from rest at the origin of coordinates.

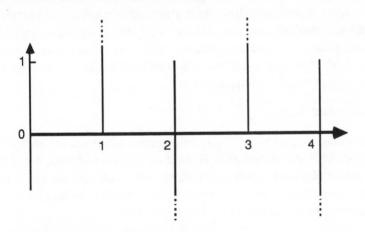

Figure 1.   Obstacle course to be negotiated.

The task is to arrive, in successive trials, at a pattern of applied force to make the object follow a path from the origin to meet the line $x = 4$, avoiding barriers on the way. Barriers are represented by vertical lines shown broken at one end to represent continuation to infinity. Because part of the line $x = 4$ is a barrier, the termination of the path must be such that y is not less than unity. The aim is then to modify the pattern of applied forces so that the trajectory is completed in minimum time.

Ideally, to conform to what has been said before, the applied force should be variable in both magnitude and direction along the trajectory, subject only to an upper bound on magnitude. Once again, simplification of these conditions has been allowed in the present study, as detailed below.

5.3.1 Digital Simulation

The simulation of a dynamic system such as this, on a digital computer, reduces to that of finding a numerical solution to a set of simultaneous first-order differential equations. Methods for doing this are well known and are discussed by Ralston and Rabinowitz (1978) and many others. Their application to simulation is discussed by Andrew (1985).

All of the methods depend on subdividing the range of the independent variable (normally time, in simulations of physical systems) into small *integration steps*. The approximation to the continuous situation improves as the step-size is reduced, and the main source of error of the method is correspondingly reduced.

Numerical methods for solving differential equations are important in the current discussion since they provide a link between digital computing and continuous systems. However, it has proved possible to avoid them in the experimental studies discussed below, with a consequent saving of computing time. Avoiding these methods also obviates any worry about the adequacy of the means of estimating the error and adjusting the step size. If the data determining the trajectory had been stored according to methods (b) or (c), it would not have been possible to use this simplification.

5.3.2 Simplified Scheme

The numerical-integration method is only needed where the differential equations have not been solved analytically. If, over an interval of travel, the force applied to the moving object is constant, the equations of motion are easily solved.

For a particle of unit mass, acted on by a focce a in (say) the x-direction, with a coefficient of damping equal to b, we have:

$$\ddot{x} = a - b\dot{x} \tag{1}$$

We may suppose that the particle starts at time $t = 0$, in position x_0 and with velocity $\dot{x}_0$. The undamped case ($b = 0$) has to be treated separately from the damped one, but solutions for both are obtained by elementary methods.

In the undamped case we have:

$$\dot{x} = \dot{x}_0 + at \tag{2}$$

$$x = x_0 + \dot{x}_0 t + at^2/2 \tag{3}$$

In the damped case the solution is of the form

$$x = (a/b)t + k_1 \exp(-bt) + k_2 \tag{4}$$

and appropriate substitutions allow the evaluation of the constants as:

$$k_1 = (a/b) - \dot{x}_0)/b; \quad k_2 = x_0 - k_1 \tag{5}$$

so that:

$$\dot{x} = (a/b) - k_1 b \exp(-bt) \tag{6}$$

In the model represented in Fig. 1, the interval of x from 0 to 4 units was divided into 16 intervals, and the force applied to the particle was held constant over each interval. On the assumption that the particle always moved from left to right, the intervals could be considered in turn in this order. For the interval from $x = 0$ to 0.25, the initial conditions are:

$$x_0 = 0; \quad y_0 = 0; \quad \dot{x}_0 = 0; \quad \dot{y}_0 = 0; \quad t = 0$$

In either Eqn.(3) or Eqn. (6), as appropriate, the x-component of the accelerating force can be substituted for a and 0.25 for x, and the equation solved for t. The solution gives the value for t_1, the time required to traverse the interval. This is substituted to allow evaluation of $\dot{x}_1$. In the undamped case the equation to be solved for t is a quadratic, but in the damped case it has to be solved by successive approximation. In either case, provision has to be made for non-existence of a finite real solution, since some values of applied force will prevent the particle from negotiating the segment. However, under the experimental condition to be described this did not actually happen.

All the equations (1-6) apply also to the y-direction, with the y-component of the accelerating force substituted for a, and appropriate initial values used. k_1 and k_2 must be evaluated afresh. The value of t_1 obtained above can be substituted to allow evaluation of y_1 and $\dot{y}_1$. The final values for the first interval become the initial ones for the next, going from $x = 0.25$ to 0.5. The second interval is treated similarly to the first, and so on over the rest of the trajectory.

Referred to 16 segments of path in this way, the control problem has 32 degrees of freedom. In order to simplify matters the magnitude of the applied force was made to be the same over the entire trajectory, with a value referred to as a. In the r-th segment the x-component of the force, corresponding to the variable designated by a in Eqns. (1-6), is $a \cos \theta_r$, and the y-component is $a \sin \theta_r$. The problem then has 17 degrees of freedom, namely the 16 angles plus the force a.

As a further simplification, the θ values were restricted to the range $-\pi/2$ to $+\pi/2$. Instead of imposing explicit bounds on the variables representing directions, they were stored, not directly as angles, but as the tangents, understood to refer to angles in the required range.

The problem is to adjust these 17 variables so that the particle traverses the course in as short a time as possible. The solution depends on the coefficient of damping, b, and to allow comparison the runs reported in detail here were with a uniform setting of $b = 0.5$. In the undamped case, the shape of the path followed by the particle is unaffected by the value of a, so if a set of values could be found that allowed the course to be completed, the time would be reduced by making a as large as possible. However, no set of values was found that allowed the course to be completed with $b = 0$.

For runs with damping, the hope was to find an adjustment procedure that would imitate human skill acquisition in manual tasks. In doing this it would reduce the value of a until it succeeded in completing the course, and then it would gradually increase a, trimming the θ-values (stored as tangents) as necessary to maintain a collision-free path. This should reduce the transit time.

The adjustment method to be described showed the required behaviour, but did not greatly increase a. It also halted the improvement well short of the optimum. Results are given in section 5.5.

5.4 AUTOMATIC OPTIMIZATION

Since the simulation procedure evaluates the outcome on the basis of 17 independent variables, it can be coupled to one of the standard optimization methods such as that of Rosenbrock.

In fact, as will be shown, complications arise in trying to apply an optimization method to this task, and it is necessary to adapt the method in ways that depend on a 'common sense' view of the problem. Thus the optimization method provides a basis on which to superimpose techniques having a flavour closer to that of traditional AI. These are discussed as *heuristic extensions* in section 5.4.2.

Intuitively, the automatic optimization procedure does not seem to have much in common with human problem-solving. Like the process of modelling by regression analysis, numerical optimization often achieves a result that is useful in practice, but in a brute-force way that does not seem particularly 'intelligent'. On the other hand, as discussed earlier, it models some aspects of 'intelligence' in an abstract way.

In the speeding-up robot, numerical optimization must play a part at some stage, since the trajectory must be precisely 'tuned' for minimum transit-time. It is possible that the initial trajectory has some quite unnecessary kinks in it—if it was generated under manual control, for exmple, the human operator may have sneezed or had his elbow joggled, and the stored information controlling the motion would retain effects of this.

As the robot speed is increased and the path becomes more ballistic, the deflections representing these kinks will decrease, but for optimal performance they should be eliminated entirely. Numerical optimization would achieve this, though so might a method based on a heuristic rule stating that the trajectory should be as smooth as possible.

In comparing automatic methods with human problem-solving, it is necessary to distinguish two sets of conditions under which a human may operate. He may be operating in the same sort of real-world environment as a robot—that is to say, he may actually wish to pick up a pencil or steer a car. Alternatively, he may be watching a computer display corresponding to Fig. 1, on which successive trajectories of an imaginary particle are traced out, with the person able to adjust the 17 (or 32) parameters by appropriate entries at a keyboard or other input device. It is, of course, much easier to indulge in introspection in the latter situation than in the former. The degree of correspondence between the heuristic principles used in the two situations can only be decided by experiment.

In the computer-display situation, the part of the problem-solving process that can be brought to consciousness has a strong content of means-ends analysis, and the setting up of subgoals in a manner very like that of the *general problem solver* of Newall, Shaw and Simon (1959). An attempt at a verbal record of a part of the process might be something like the following:

> "Since the aim is to complete the course as quickly as possible, I'll try applying a larger accelerating force. The particle will swing wide on the curves, and the first place this is likely to produce a collision is at barrier n. I need to consider the subgoal of avoiding a collision there, preferably without reducing the accelerating force. If the direction of the applied force can be altered so as to deflect the particle appropriately, somewhere in the interval preceding barrier n, I'll try that. If there is no possibility of steering corrections in this interval (because the modulus of the angle is everywhere close to its limit of $\pi/2$) and the barrier is not the first, I have to consider the subgoal of adjusting the steering prior to barrier $(n - 1)$, such that the particle passes it with a y-component of velocity that helps it to pass barrier n. It is probably best that the particle passes close to barrier $(n - 1)$, since the short path length is likely to be advantageous. In the early part of the interval preceding barrier $(n - 1)$ I have to steer the particle as though

to swing wide of that barrier, and then to pull it back towards it ...".

It can be seen by comparing Fig. 2(a) and Fig. 2(b) that it can be advantageous, in order to clear the second barrier, to deflect the path in the opposite direction, prior to the first barrier, and similarly for later barriers. An alternative way of expressing the heuristic would be to say that the maximum curvature of the path should be minimized. (In this latter form the heuristic is consciously applied by drivers of vehicles wishing to move quickly without provoking a skid.)

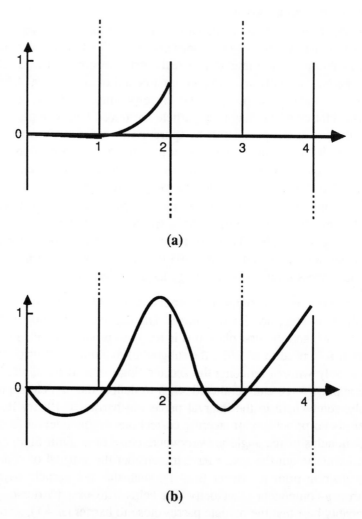

(a)

(b)

Figure 2.   (a) Path without preparatory deflection.   (b) Path with preparatory deflection.

Although the above section of a hypothetical protocol strongly suggests that a GPS-like goal structure is involved, further consideration shows that it is not the whole story. Quantitative, and hence continuous, considerations play a part in the heuristic choices, for example in deciding whether the effect of pursuing a particular subgoal is likely to be large enough to be useful. Also, qualitative decisions such as 'deflect the path downwards' need to be associated with some quantitative guidance to determine the magnitude of the change. Where the downward deflection has to be compensated by a later one in the reverse direction, as in the first interval of Fig. 2(b), the magnitude of the downward deflection should be governed by some rough estimate of the amount of compensation possible in the later part of the interval.

The heuristics used for qualitative guidance need not indicate final values, since there is a sequence of adjustments. However, the success of the adjustment process depends on a complex interplay of continuous and discrete aspects.

The above discussion is influenced by the writer's lack of success in trying to find an algorithm for this problem purely from the starting point of a GPS-like goal structure. Obviously, this does not mean that no successful algorithm is possible on this basis, but it suggests the problem is non-trivial and worthy of further attention. As argued earlier, some sort of numerical optimization technique must play a part at some stage if the precisely-optimal solution is to be reached.

Some of the heuristic rules providing quantitative guidance are likely to indicate quantitative relationships between variables. For example, an increase in the downward deflecting force in the early part of the first interval in Fig. 2(b) has to be compensated by an increase in the upward force later in the interval. The existence of such a relationship can be recognized by reformulating the problem in terms of a new set of variables. One such variable might represent the magnitude of the transient downward deflection in the first interval, and a change in it would impose changes of opposite sign in the deflecting forces applied in the early and later parts of the interval.

The reformulation of problems in terms of new sets of variables is an important feature of Rosenbrock's method of numerical optimization. In the derivation of the method the reformulation is discussed in terms of ridges of the 'hill' to be climbed in a multi-dimensional space. Such ridges indicate relationships between the independent variables like those recognized as being useful in connection with a GPS-type solution. As discussed in section 5.2.3, the reorientation in multi-dimensional space may model some aspects of 'intelligence'.

In section 5.5, results will be presented from a modification of Rosenbrock's method embodying some GPS-like features. First, a brief account is given of the method itself, and its adaptation to the present problem.

5.4.1 Rosenbrock's Method

The method described by Rosenbrock (1960) was his choice after a long series of trials of alternatives. For some hill-climbing problems the choice of method is not critical since almost any method will reach the summit of a smooth round hill. Difficulty arises when the approach to the optimum is along a sharp ridge, especially a curving one. The process is readily visualized in connection with the climbing of three-dimensional hills (i.e. hills growing up from a 2-D map) but the same considerations apply in space of higher dimensionality.

It is well known that a hill-climbing procedure may halt prematurely if it can only change one variable at a time. This can be visualized on a 3-D hill by supposing that a (blind) climber has arrived on the crest of a sharp ridge running north-east and rising gently towards the summit. Exploration in the north-south direction shows he has reached an extremum, and so does exploration in the east-west direction, so if he is only able to change one variable at a time he has no way of knowing he has not reached the summit. If the ridge is not razor-sharp, it may happen that a small displacement northward or eastward produces an increase in altitude, so he may be able to proceed upward in a series of small steps to the north and to the east, but his progress will certainly be tedious.

Rosenbrock's method goes through a succession of *stages*, and in each stage it follows the above one-variable-at-a-time method. However, it is only in the first stage that the 'variables' correspond to the directions of the coordinate axes. At the end of each stage a new set of orthogonal directions is chosen, the principal one being aligned with the total progress of the operating point in the previous stage. The intention is that, if the way to the optimum is along a sharp ridge (or the higher-dimensional equivalent of a ridge), the principal direction comes to be aligned with the ridge. If the ridge curves, the alignment is with a part of it already traversed, but it is likely to be fairly close to that of the part of it lying ahead.

Only one direction is determined by the advance in the previous stage. If n is the number of independent variables, the direction is represented by an n-dimensional vector. The assignment of the other $(n - 1)$ orthogonal directions, at the end of each stage, is made in the original program by the use of the Gram-Schmidt orthogonalization method. An alternative method of orthogonalization, more enomomical in computing time, is given by Powell (1968). The two methods are not equivalent; they do not in general give the same set of orthogonal directions, but there is no obvious reason to suggest that one is preferable to the other except on the grounds of economy of computing effort.

In an experimental comparison in a specific context (Andrew 1969) it was found that the use of Powell's method allowed a slightly closer approach to the optimum than did the use of the Gram-Schmidt method, but it is not known whether this advantage holds generally. In the runs reported here, orthogonal-ization, if it was done at all, was according to the Gram-Schmidt method as originally described by Rosenbrock.

The Gram-Schmidt method is realized in PROCEDURE *orth* of the Pascal program in Appendix A, adapted from a similar one in an earlier publication (Andrew 1985). The orthognalization principle is explained in Appendix B.

Within any one stage the method makes a sequence of *trials*, in each of which the operating point is moved along one of the orthogonal directions and the objective function is re-evaluated. If the step is successful, i.e. if it leads to an increase, or no change in the objective function it is retained. If it is a failure the operating point returns to its previous position. The sequence of trials cycles through the n orthogonal directions until the conditions are appropriate for ending the stage. A stage is terminated when there has been at least one successful move, and at least one failure, in each of the n directions.

In any numerical optimization procedure, the size of the *steps* must be adjustd to suit the problem. In the early stages of search, relatively large steps are desirable, but for final convergence smaller ones are needed. In Rosenbrock's method a step size is associated with each of the n directions (and is carried over to the direction having the same position in the list, when the directions are reassigned at the end of a stage). The initial step size is set rather arbitrarily by the programmer (to 0.1 in the present study).

Following a trial that is a success, the step size associated with the direction of change is multiplied by a factor of three. Following a failure it is multiplied by -0.5. This means that, so long as the operating point is moving towards the optimum, it is made to advance in ever-increasing strides, but when it has passed the peak and begins to go downhill it doubles back and reduces the step length. If the steps come to straddle the optimum, the step size is automatically reduced to give fine adjustment.

Rosenbrock argues that the condition for terminating a stage must eventually be met. He assumes that the objective function is influenced by a move of the operating point along each of the directions, and that it has a maximum that is not at infinity. It follows that a series of moves, without reversal, in any one of the directions must eventually result in a failure. It is not so obvious that a success must eventually be enountered, since if the operating point is positioned precisely at the optimal position, any move must result in failure if it is is large enough to make any change at all. However, since the magnitude of the step size is halved following each failure, it eventually becomes so small that the objective function, as computed digitally, is unaltered by taking the step, and the step is then counted as a success.

In the above account of Rosenbrock's method, nothing has been said about constraints on the independent variables. In principle, constraints can be in-corporated in the objective function. Let x be the set of independent variables $x_1, x_2, \ldots, x_n$, and let $v(x)$ be the objective function to be maximized. Then constraints can be introduced by defining an effective objective function $u(x)$ to equal $v(x)$ where no constraint is violated, but otherwise to have a value lower than any within the permitted region. An optimization problem subject to constraints can be reduced to one without constraints by changing the objective function.

In practice, things are not quite so simple, because the objective function obtained in this way is likely to have very sharp ridges to be traversed on the way to the optimum. The ridges have a vertical cliff on one side, and although the method has been devised with sharp ridges in mind, it does not perform very well when required to traverse ridges of this kind. In the original paper the difficulty is ameliorated by a number of ingenious devices which can be ignored for the present purpose. A great deal of attention has been given to this aspect of the problem by other workers, as reviewed by Box (1965). Box also describes a totally different approach to the problem of constrained optimization.

In the present case the objective function is the transit time (to be mini-mized), subject to the constraint that there are no collisions with barriers. This is a constraint of a rather different kind from that visualized by Rosenbrock and by Box, since the only way of deciding whether it is violated is by initiating the same process as required to evaluate the transit time. It also differs in having a range of degrees of severity of violation, since it is presumably a worse violation to collide with the first barrier than to collide with a later one. By the nature of the problem, the constraint is more intimately associated with the objective function than is usual in applications of numerical optimization.

5.4.2 Optimizing a Trajectory

The computer program used to implement Rosenbrock's method was a modifi-cation of that shown in Andrew (1985). The first step was to modify some numerical constants appearing in the program, so that it would operate in 17-dimensional space. (The original was limited to 10 dimensions.)

It was necessary to embody the simulation procedure, as discussed in section 5.3.3, in a Pascal procedure named *eval*, this being the means of evaluating the objective function. The procedure *eval* replaces the simple function of the same name, relating to a totally different problem, in the original illustrative program.

It would have been possible to arrange for *eval* to return a *real* numerical value, but the operation of the program is much more transparent if the objective function is evaluated as a Pascal *record* having four *fields*. Three of these represent the objective function and the fourth is, strictly speaking, redundant but included for convenience. The *record* type is defined as follows:

TYPE evaln = RECORD   reach: integer
                         miss, tim: real;
                         success: boolean
          END;

The procedure *eval* assigns to *reach* an integer representing the number (0 to 16) of segments of the trajectory completed. If the accelerating force, a, is zero or negative, *reach* is set to zero and the simulation procedure is not carried out. If it should happen that the simulation halts in some segment because there is no real finite solution to the equation to be solved for t (see section 5.3.3), *reach* indicates the number of segments successfuly traversed. If the simulation halts because a barrier has been met, *reach* has the value 4, 8, 12 or 16 depending on the barrier reached, and it has the value 16 if the course is completed without collision.

If there is no collision, *miss* has value zero, but if there is a collision with a barrier, *miss* gives the magnitude of the distance between the point of impact and the edge of the barrier. The time taken to reach the point at which the trajectory terminates is assigned to *tim*. The redundant field *success* has value *true* if the course is successfully completed, i.e. if *reach* = 16 and *miss* = 0.

In the program for the Rosenbrock method, the only use made of the numerical evaluations is for comparison. Prior to a trial step along one of the orthogonal directions, the value of the objective function is stored as u. The value after taking the step is stored as ul. In the original program, where u and ul are *real*, the success of the step is judged as the value of the boolean function $(ul \text{ } ¿= u)$. Where the objective function is returned as a *record* of type *evaln*, u and ul must be of this type, and success is judged as the value of $gteq(ul, u)$, where the Pascal function *gteq* is defined as follows:

FUNCTION gteq(x, y: evaln): boolean;
BEGIN   IF x.reach <> y.reach THEN
         gteq:= x.reach > y.reach
        ELSE IF x.miss <> y.miss THEN
         gteq:= x.miss < y.miss
        ELSE gteq:= x.tim <= y.tim
END;

In other words, the three fields *reach*, *miss* and *tim* are compared using lexical priority. The inclusion of *miss* is advantageous because the optimization would otherwise encounter the *mesa effect* (Minsky and Selfridge 1961) when the trajectory ended in a collision with a barrier.

It soon beame clear that certain other common-sense modifications of the method were needed. In the early stages of optimization, if the starting values of the variables do not allow the trajectory to be completed, the variables that control the steering in the non-traversed later segments have no effect whatsoever on the objective function. Consequently, every trial change in one of them is counted as a *success*, according to Rosenbrock's criterion, and the step sizes associated with them become enormous, as do the values of the variables themselves.

The criterion for ending a stage cannot be met until there is a trial in which all 16 segments are traversed, because until then there is no way that the variable associated with the final segment can produce an indication of *failure*. This means that the search for a valid trajectory does not have the advantage of Rosenbrock's reassignment of directions.

The remedy is to declare an integer variable *maxreach*, initially set to zero, and updated to show the maximum value assigned to the *reach* field in any evaluation. The optimization method is readily modified to operate on a subset of the variables, provided the subset comes first in the order of listing. In most runs the accelerating force a was a variable, and was then stored as $x[1]$, the first of the 17 variables, of which the remaining 16 were steering variables associated with the segments of path. In these runs, the operation of the optimization method was restricted to a subset of the variables whose number was (maxreach +1). This number was held as *effvars* (number of *effective variables*). In runs in which a was not variable, or was given special treatment, it was stored as $x[17]$ and the operation of the optimization method was restricted by setting *effvars* equal to *maxreach*. The condition for terminating a stage was that at least one success and one failure had occurred for each of the effective directions (*effvar* in number), not for the total of 17 directions.

The orthogonalization process readily lends itself to operation with a subset of variables. The 17 orthogonal directions are represented as unit vectors in 17-dimensional space, in rows of a 17×17 square matrix. Initially this is set to be a unit matrix. Provided the value of *effvars* never decreases, an appropriate result is then obtained by letting the orthogonalization process operate on the upper-left square matrix of order *effvars* within the larger one, the rest of the latter remaining unchanged.

In the operation of the method with these enhancements, it was observed that progress would sometimes almost halt when there was the end of a stage shortly after the path was adjusted so as to clear one of the barriers, but to collide with the next one. This stagnation would occur, even though the steering variables associated with the newly-traversed section of the path had values near to zero and so could have been altered in a direction that would help steer the particle towards clearing the next barrier.

The trouble is that the end of the stage has come at an inopportune time, when very little movement has been made in the directions of the newly-admitted variables. The reassignment of directions therefore effectively 'buries' these variables by combining them with others, even though the variables in their raw state are highly relevant to surmounting the next barrier.

The remedy is to reset various records, as though at the beginning of a new stage, whenever *maxreach* is incremented. The record of progress of the operating point during the stage, and the record of occurrences of success and failure in trials along each of the directions, are reset. With these modifications the optimization process was successful in finding a path past the barriers, and in achieving some subsequent increase in speed of transit.

One of the points to be investigated was the extent to which Rosenbrock's reassignment of directions is useful in this situation, and the program allowed the option of eliminating this and operating entirely on the 'raw' variables.

5.4.3 Heuristic Extensions

These modifications of the optimization method have some claim to be described as heuristics. They certainly depend, (as does Rosenbrock's original derivation of his method) on the kind of common-sense argument that is characteristic of human intelligence. To a person, it is obvious that if a trajectory ends due to a collision at a particular point, nothing is gained by adjusting variables that can have no effect until after that point has been passed.

It is perhaps not entirely obvious, but certainly intuitively plausible, that the change in the situation when a barrier is passed is such that certain data representing cumulative experience should be re-initialized. The modification ensuring this can be seen as an example of a very general heuristic principle, to the effect that it is likely to be useful to reset statistical data when there is a significant change in the situation.

Two further heuristic estensions of the method have been considered. Each of them allows, in a very simple way, a hierarchical goal structure reminiscent of that of GPS.

Of the 17 variables, that representing the accelerating force is in different units from the others, and clearly is of a different kind. Once a full-length trajectory has been achieved, a change in a is likely to require adjustment of many of the other variables to preserve the collision-free performance, whereas a change in one of the other variables can perhaps be balanced by altering others near it.

A person trying to solve this optimization problem, at least in the computer-interaction mode discussed in section 5.3.3, tends to treat it hierarchically, in that a value is chosen for a, and the attempt is made to steer a course past the barriers by adjustment of the other variables. If the attempt is successful, the value fo a

is increased, otherwise decreased, and again the other variables are adjusted in the attempt to obtain a full-length trajectory. There is, in fact, an optimization nested within another optimization.

A variation of the program was prepared, operating in this dual fashion, and will be referred to as *Rosdual*. It is, of course, necessary to have a *stopping rule* for the nested optimization, and such rules are a feature of practical optimization methods. A stopping rule is a specific example of an *administrative* heuristic as discussed by Minsky (1959a). In the program as implemented, the nested optimization was stopped after a preset number of trials. The current state of the 'outer'optimization , including the set of orthogonal directions and associated step lengths, was stored before initiating the nested optimization. If the latter produced no improvement, a return was made to this previous state.

Another form of hierarchical optimization was tried, in order to induce a deflection of the path prior to a barrier, as in Fig. 2(b). The method, in its non-hierarchical form, never showed any sign of having 'discovered' the advantage of this. A version of the program was written in which, whenever there was an increase in *maxreach*, corresponding to the path passing one barrier for the first time but colliding with the next, the optimization conditions were stored (some of them having been reset as discussed in the previous section), and a nested optimization was invoked.

The nested optimization was made with *maxreach* held at at the position of the barrier just surmounted, i.e. to a value smaller by four than that applying in the 'outer' optimization. For the inner optimization the objective function was as before, except that the *tim* field was made to hold an indication of the y-derivative at the end of the length of path indicated by *maxreach* (or earlier termination). For the second barrier the value returned was the y-derivative and for the first and third barriers it was the negative of this. This ensured that minimization of the entry in the *tim* field corresponded to maximization of the y-component of velocity that should be advantageous in passing the next obstacle.

The program (referred to as *Rosderiv*) was written to give the option of using the time derivative (i.e. the value of $\dot{y}$ at the end of the path) or of gradient (the ratio $\dot{y}/\dot{x}$). Results are given in the next section.

In some runs it was felt that Rosenbrock's rule for terminating a stage was unduly conservative. With 17 variables there are 34 conditions to be met (a success and a failure in moving along each of the 17 directions), and sometimes a stage goes on for a very long time with 33 of them satisfied. There is probably an advantage in terminating a stage after some preset number of trials, or when some fraction of the 34 conditions is met. If this is done, however, the orthogonalization procedure has to be modified to allow for the case where progress

In the earlier runs it was arranged that the evaluation (simulation) procedure returned a *reach* value of zero if the value of the accelerating force a, was zero or negative. For the runs with fixed a of value 0.6 or more, the value zero was returned for *reach* if the magnitude of any of the 16 steering variables was greater than 100. An angle having a tangent of 100 differs from a right angle by approximately 0.01 of a radian, or just over half a degree.

5.5.2 Rosderiv

Runs were made with a hierarchical program, as described in section 5.4.3, in which nested optimizations were carried out, with the goal of bringing the y-derivative towards an appropriate extremum. The stopping condition for the nested optimization was simply the completion of 100 trials.

In these runs, the initial value of the steering variable for the first segment of path was set to -1 rather than to zero, since otherwise the first nested optimization would be unable to deflect the path downward in the manner of Fig. 2(b).

Judged by their immediate effects, the nested optimizations had the apperaance of being advantageous. At the return to the 'outer' optimization, the evaluation obtained by adopting the final values of the variables from the nested one was always preferable to that obtained just prior to its initiation. This was because the nested optimization reduced the value of the *miss* field of the evaluation, by bringing the path closer to the edge of the following barrier.

Nevertheless, the overall performance of the runs of this program version did not improve on those of the standard one. A run in which the nested optimizations were with reference to the gradient (derivative with respect to x) led to the course being completed in the 470th trial (including 300 trials in the nested optimizations), but with a transit time of 60 units. This transit time had not been improved upon by the end of the run of 1000 trials.

The result suggested that it might be better to let the nested optimization be with reference to the time derivative rather than the gradient. However, the first trial, with the full set of 17 variables, failed to surmount the third barrier. Other runs with fixed values of a, allowed completion of the course, but did not improve on the transit times of the standard program.

5.5.3 Comparison with Manual Adjustment

By manual interaction with a screen display, a set of values allowing traversal of the entire course was found to be as follows:

Accelerating force, $a = 1$

Steering variables (tangents of angles), 16 values as follows:

$-1\ 3\ 3\ 3\quad 10\ 10\ -10\ -10\quad -10\ -3\ 10\ 10\quad 6\ 0\ 0\ 1$

The transit time with these values was 9.75 units. They were used as starting values for the standard method, as in the first run reported in section 5.5. After a run with 1000 trials in nine stages, a traversal time of 7.10 units was achieved with an accelerating force of 1.21.

This lowest-of-all transit time was achieved by the use of automatic optimization to improve on a solution found manually. The fact that it is substantailly better than anything achieved by a program alone suggests that the manual adjustment utilized a heuristic principle not modelled in any of the computational methods.

In general the results of the runs did not produce trajectories having deflections of the type illustrated in Fig. 2(b), occurring ahead of a barrier n as a preparation for negotiating barrier $(n+1)$. Such deflections were a feature of the manually-adjusted path, and were not destroyed in the subsequent automatic improvement. Their occurrence in the early part of the trajectory was deliberately encouraged in the runs of the Rosderiv version of the program, by setting the first steering variable, initially, to -1. However, the adjustments made during the run often eliminated this supposed advantage by bringing the early part of the trajectory close to the x-axis.

Strangely enough, the one run in which the program had the appearance of having discovered for itself the advantage of these preparatory deflections was the one with a fixed value of a equal to 1.2, shown in the second-last line of Table 1. However, the curious nonmonotonicity of the results in the table suggests that this run performed *worse* than might have been expected from interpolation from other runs.

These results will be discussed further in the next chapter. They support the contention that the problem area to which they refer is non-trivial, and although they do not indicate an elegant or final solution they at least provide a basis for comparison for further studies.

6

Conclusions

6.1 INTROSPECTION ON CONTINUITY

It has been argued here, from various viewpoints, that there is an important connection between the processing of continuous information to meet the needs of biological regulation, and continuous processing 'behind the scenes' in conscious symbolic thinking.

As was acknowledged in connection with language and jokes in Chapter 3, continuity also enters into conscious thought quite overtly. People are very ready to form continuous models of parts of their environments. Even when the modelling is at the abstract level of mathematics, the first introduction is usually in terms of continuous variables. For most people, the idea of computation with numbers, and later with algebraic symbols understood to have numerical significance, is more intuitive than formal logic. (The protagonists of some modern ideas on mathematics teaching may dispute this, perhaps referring to the successful introduction of *set theory* at an early stage of mathematical education. However, one of the arguments advanced in favour of the early teaching of set theory is that it provides, via the *Peano postulates*, a basis for a theory of numbers and hence for continuity 'in the large'.)

Although the symbolism of mathematics clearly brings it into the domain of symbolic processing, ideas of continuity lie behind it, at least in its elementary stages and in certain lines of development such as differential and integral calculus. It is interesting that Boole turned to the ideas expounded in his *Laws of Thought* from a study of differential equations, and it is possible that some illuminating comments on the relationship of finite concepts to continuous variables could be found in his account of this development.

A related topic that has received much attention is the relationship of atomic theory to classical physics. For practical purposes, the gap has been satisfactorily bridged by theoreticians including Boltzmann and Schrödinger under the heading of *statistical mechanics*. However, as shown in a recent biography of Schrödinger by Moore (1989), these workers were also concerned with the philosophical nature of the continuity that distinguishes the classical theory from the atomic one. Boltzmann is on record as claiming that the differential equations of classical physics constitute a "model or thought picture severely abstracted from observations". This was said prior to important work by Schrödinger which established the basis of *statistical mechanics* and supported the view that the continuity implicit in the equations is a property of the physical world rather than merely of subjective experience.

6.2 RELEVANCE OF ROBOTICS

It would be surprising if the 'hidden'continuous aspects of conceptual thinking represented a fresh development unconnected with primitive continuous behaviour. The argument of this book is that they should instead be seen as a residue, or genetic legacy, of the latter.

If this 'genetic legacy' view has any validity, it is reasonable to suppose that increased understanding will come from examination of the evolutionary process by which thinking has become increasingly concept-based. Suggestions have been made about the origins of conceptual processing in connection with the tail-flicks of unicellular organisms, and the commitment to different behaviour modes of primitive nervous systems. At a very much later stage of evolution the brain emerged as a development of motor control, and eventually this led to the human cerebral cortex with its powerful capacity for concept-based processing.

Traditional AI studies are aimed at joining this evolutionary process at an advanced stage by emulating its late achievements. The field of robotics focusses attention on developments that came earlier, and promotes an integrated view of the evolution of intelligence. It has been mentioend that Churchland (1986) supports her arguments by reference to an imaginary sensory robot. It is also encouraging to find that Pearl (1984), in his *prologue*, refers to car-driving as his first example of an activity depending on *heuristics*. His subsequent theoretical treatment refers to very different task environments, but the importance of the continous one is tacitly acknowledged.

6.3 WHERE NOW?

The experimental results quoted in section 5.5 suggest that even this simple 'toy problem' presents a significant challenge. The solution of problems of this sort entails the complex interaction of continuous computation with discrete decision-making that we want to examine.

There is of course no guarantee that Rosenbrock's method of optimization provides the best starting-point from which to approach the trajectory problem. On the other hand, as argued in Chapter 5, something in the nature of a numerical optimization procedure has to enter at some stage. Also, as argued in sections 5.2.3 and 5.4, the reorientation in multi-dimensional space, characteristic of the Rosenbrock method, can be seen as the discovery of relevant properties of the environment. The representations of these can be said to constitute simple heuristics which have been elicited by the method.

Only very simple heuristics can be elicited in this way. For the present purpose, however, a more significant limitation is the fact that, once discovered, the heuristic is only stored transiently. The optimization procedure, as implemented, only stores one set of orthogonal directions at a time.

The aim, of course, is to find an AI-type solution, i.e. one that is robust and adaptive, so as to emulate the human capability for finding an expeditious path round arbitrary configurations of obstacles, and of readily adapting to various physical characteristics of the situation. The heuristic principles underlying any such solution can presumably be represented in terms of *means-ends analysis*. The usual sample of dialogue used to illustrate this can be adapted to the situation:

> "I want the trajectory to go the full length without a collision, and as rapidly as possible. At present it collides with barrier no. 1. What change in control forces would avoid this? ... "

The avoidance of barrier no. 1 is set as an initial subgoal, and once it has been achieved it is likely that the trajectory ends at barrier no. 2, so a further subgoal refers to surmounting it, and so on. However, there is a very important difference between this situation and the kind to which the GPS is applicable. In the GPS (theorem-proving or graph-traversal) situation, once a goal is achieved it stays that way. It may prove to be irrelevant to the overall task, in that the final solution does not utilize it, but its validity cannot be contested.

In contrast, the subgoals in trajectory-finding may compete with each other. The adjustments intended to let the trajectory surmount barrier no. 2 are very likely to cause it to collide with barrier no. 1. It is necessary to monitor the continuous validity of subgoals already achieved.

Where the degree of success is indicated by a single (albeit structured) objective function, as in the experiments reported in the previous chapter, the continued validity of the earler subgoals is effectively monitored by evaluation. However, the method operates in such a way that any violation of the earlier subgoal causes the change in applied forces to be promptly rescinded.

A person making the adjustments (relative, say, to subgoal no. r) does not necessarily rescind a change that causes a violation of an earlier subgoal Instead, he often returns to the earlier subgoal and attempts further adjustments relevant to it, probably trying to cause as little interference as possible with the change just made in connection with subgoal no. r. If he cannot restore the validity of the earlier subgoal he has to rescind, or reduce, the change made in connection with the later subgoal.

It can be seen that a form of *backtracking* is involved, but it differs significantly from that used in GPS, where a return to an earlier subgoal means that a new branch of the development tree is to be explored. The decision to backtrack in GPS is effectively a GOTO instruction. In contrast, the trajectory-finding algorithm requires a form of backtracking that is similar to the calling of a *procedure* in an ALGOL-type language. This means that the attempt to re-achieve an early subgoal can be nested within the attempt to achieve the later one.

Information relating to the adjustment strategy must be stored separately for each of the subgoals, including, eventually, that of minimizing transit time. It is for this reason that the restriction of Rosenbrock's method to storing its heuristic information only transiently is a serious disadvantage. Instead, the information should be stored separately for each of the subgoals.

If the information is stored in the form of multi-dimensional vectors, it is possible that the principle underlying the Gram-Schmidt procedure (Appendix B) could be applied to let adjustment relative to one subgoal be made with minimal disturbance of another subgoal. From two vectors, A and B, say, it is generally possible to obtain a direction that is orthogonal to B, but as close as possible to A, by subtracting from A the vector constituting its projection onto B. The resulting vector might usefully indicate how to adjust variables to try to achieve the subgoal to which A refers, with little disturbance to that to which B refers.

It is possible to imagine situations in which each of the two kinds of back-tracking would be needed (i.e. backtracking having the character of GOTO and backtracking having the character of a procedure call — a term to denote the latter might be *backvisiting*). This will certainly occur if the space in which trajectories can lie is multiply-connected. This means that a given feasible trajectory cannot be continuously deformed to match all other feasible trajectories, so a choice has to be made between topologically-distinct routes.

Even in connection with these simple 'toy' problems, the set of heuristics needed to guide the solution process can be quite complicated. When, in the course of making adjustments with regard to subgoal no. r, say, an earlier subgoal is violated, the adjustment process need not invariably return to the earlier goal by *backvisiting*. The alternative is to reduce the change which produced the violation, and the choice between the two must depend on further heuristics. These heuristics would no doubt take account of the number of other possibilities open to the adjustment process in pursuing subgoal no. r, and of an estimate of the *tractability* of the earlier goal, indicating the likelihood that it would indeed be re-established during the *backvisit.*

It should be possible to develop a set of heuristics applicable to these problems probably of similar complexity to those underlying the general problem solver, but different in character. When dealing with trajectories seen on a screen, people solve the problems with remarkable ease, at least in the early stages of finding a feasible and reasonably-smooth path. It would be worth while to follow the example of Newell, Shaw and Simon (1959) and to record the responses of subjects during the solution process. The 'protocols' would then be analysed to infer the strategies employed. It is also useful to examine records of human perfomance in direct physical control of trajectories.

There seems to be, here, a large, untrodden and potentially-valuable area of investigation. Even at this simple level many intriguing questions arise. Much more is needed to interpret the principles underlying, for example, the acts of judgement involved in complex skills like driving, but these may eventually be illuminated, if not resolved, by examining heuristic methods applicable to trajectory problems as considered above.

6.4 PALAEO-AI

It is obvious that the development of artificially intelligent systems cannot exactly model natural evolution, if only because results are needed more quickly. If the comparison is with the whole process of evolution from the time of the earliest known fossil records, estimated as three thousand million years ago, the factor by which we want results more quickly is at least 10^8. Nevertheless, since natural intelligence has achieved results that we are currently unable to emulate in artifacts, it is worth while to look for a way forward by considering possible routes by which the capabilities of living systems may have evolved. There is potential value in *palaeo-AI.*

The environments in which robots have to solve problems are presumably much more like those of primitive living organisms than are the other relatively abstract environments of other AI work. Their study should give insight into the environmental background of the evolution of concept-based processing. To quote Bellman and Goldberg (1984), "what is *adaptive* for any species is based on the then extant geophysical and biological world and the principles that govern the operations and interactions in these worlds."

The references that have been made here to biological evolution have ranged widely over the evolutionary scale. The origins of concept-based processing have been related to the needs of unicellular organisms, but this is at a vastly different evolutionary stage from that at which brains began to appear as a development of motor control. The references made here have been with a rather cavalier disregard for the disparity in evolutionary stage, but this can be excused by noting that, although the origins of concept-based processing are to be found in unicellular organisms, there was enormous development in later stages.

The idea that the origins of concept-based processing are to be sought in unicellular organisms is argued by Bellman and Goldberg. They suggest that "the essential question [concerning the origin of linguistic and movement abilities] is not how humans have evolved symbolic and linguistic abilities from a primitive sensorimotor function, but rather how do symbols come to exist in biological systems and what is useful and necesssary about a system of symbols for the coordination of action within animals and among animals".

These views of Bellamn and Goldberg refer to the *origins* of symbolic processing, and do not conflict with the view that it was enormously elaborated in the evolutionary development of a primitive neural sensorimotor function. It is appropriate to consider both stages of its development as underlying human intelligence.

6.5 FINALLY ...

The experimental study reported in Chapter 5 indicates that the problem is non-trivial, and provides a definite context on which to base subsequent discussion of possibilities for more powerful heuristics. These are discussed in the limited context of heuristic trajectory planning, but lead into a very exciting area of investigation and speculation because they focus on forms of intelligent activity involving both continuous regulation and heuristics.

Some of the heuristics require recognition of discrete concepts (in the pre-linguistic sense that is consistent with the reference to the emergence of *symbols* in the last quotation from Bellman and Goldberg). If, as seems likely, this development parallels biological evolution, we can claim to be studying a 'missing link' in the evolution of intelligence. It is certainly my 'hunch' that this must lead to a deeper understanding of the nature of intelligence, and the part played by continuous processes that operate subconsciously and guide conceptual thinking. As the needs of robotics force AI to interact with the real, unabstracted world in which living organisms evolved we can expect to gain more and more insight into the nature of intelligence through greater understanding of its evolution.

References

Alkon, D.L. & Farley, J. (1984) *Primary Neural Substrates of Learning and Behavioural Change*, University Press, Cambridge.

Anderson, J.A. & Hinton, G.E. (1981) Models of information processing in the brain. In: *Parallel Models of Associative Memory*, Lawrence Erlbaum, Hillsdale, New Jersey, pp. 9–48.

Andreae, P.M. & Andreae, J.H. (1978) A teachable machine in the real world, *Int. J. Man-Machine Studies* **10**, 301–312.

Andrew, A.M. (1955) Action potentials from the frog colliculus, *J. Physiol.* **130**, p. 25P.

Andrew, A.M. (1959) Learning machines. In: *Mechanisation of Thought Processes*, H.M.S.O., London, pp. 473–505.

Andrew, A.M. (1961) Self-optimising control mechanisms and some principles for more advanced learning machines. In: *Automatic and Remote Control* (IFAC Moscow Congress), Butterworth, London, pp. 818–824.

Andrew, A.M. (1965) *Significance Feedback in Neural Nets*, Report of Biological Computer Lab., Univ. of Illinois, Urbana.

Andrew, A.M. (1967a) To model or not to model, *Kybernetik* **3**, 6, 272–275.

Andrew, A.M. (1967b) Learning systems. In: Stewart, D.J. (ed.), *Automaton Theory and Learning Systems*, Academic Press, London, pp. 107–136.

Andrew, A.M. (1969) The calculation of orthogonal vectors (Letter to the Editor), *Computer Jnl.* **12**, 411.

Andrew, A.M. (1973) Significance feedback and redundancy reduction in self-organizing networks. In: Pichler, F. & Trappl, R. (eds) *Advances in Cybernetics and Systems Research 1*, Hemisphere, London, pp. 244–252.

Andrew, A.M. (1977) Cybernetics and Artificial Intelligence. In: Rose, J. & Bilciu, C. (eds) *Modern Trends in Cybernetics and Systems*, Editura Technica, Bucharest, and Springer, N.Y., pp. 477–485.

Andrew, A.M. (1978) Succinct representation in neural nets and general systems. In: Klir, G.J. (ed.) *Applied General Systems Research*, Plenum, N.Y., pp. 553–561.

Andrew, A.M. (1979) Goals and meta-goals of adaptive systems. In: Ericson, R.F. (ed.) *Improving the Human Condition–Quality and Stability in Social Systems*, SGSR, Louisville, and Springer, Berlin, pp. 444–449.

Andrew, A.M. (1980) Elementary continuity and Minsky's "heuristic connection". *Second International Meeting on A.I.*, Repino, near Leningrad. To appear in *Int. J. Systems Research and Info. Science*.

Andrew, A.M. (1981) The concept of a concept. In: Lasker, G.E. (ed.) *Applied Systems and Cybernetics*, Pergamon, N.Y., pp. 607–612.

Andrew, A.M. (1982) Logic and continuity – a systems dichotomy. In: Trappl, R. (ed.) *Cybernetics and Systems Research*, North-Holland, Amsterdam, pp. 19–22.

Andrew, A.M. (1983) *Artificial Intelligence*, Abacus, Tunbridge Wells (now Gordon & Breach, London).

Andrew, A.M. (1984) Some comments on adaptive robotics. In: Ponomaryov, V.M. (ed.) *Artificial Intelligence*, Pergamon, Oxford, pp. 239–243.

Andrew, A.M. (1985) *Computational Techniques in Operations Research*, Abacus, Tunbridge Wells (now Gordon & Breach, London).

Andrew, A.M. (1987a) How robotics expands A.I., *Robotica* **5**, 111–115. To appear in: Pugh, A., Taylor, P. & Taylor, G. *Autonomous Robots*, IFS Publications, Bedford.

Andrew, A.M. (1987b) Self-organizing systems and artificial intelligence, *Int. J. Systems Research and Info. Science* **2**, 143–151.

Andrew, A.M. (1987c) Continuous heuristics. In: Rose, J. (ed.) *Cybernetics and Systems: The Way Ahead*, Thales, Lytham St. Annes, pp. 39–43.

Andrew, A.M. (1987d) Anticipatory systems, by Robert Rosen (Book Review) *Kybernetes* **16**, pp. 57–58. To appear in *1988 General Systems Yearbook*.

Andrew, A.M. (1988) Tesselation Daisyworld – a new model of global homeostasis. In: Trappl, R. (ed.) *Cybernetics and Systems '88*, Kluwer, Dordrecht, pp. 313–320.

Andrew, A.M. (1989) *Self-Organizing Systems*, Gordon & Breach, London.

Andrew, A.M. (1990a) Letter to the Editor (Comment on paper by Galopin) *Int. J. General Systems* **16**, p. 291.

Andrew, A.M. (1990b) Discrete, continuous and stochastic neural models. Tenth European Meeting on Cybernetics and Systems Research, Vienna, April.

Andrew, A.M. & Roberts, T.D.M. (1953) A pulse-interval meter for measuring impulse frequency directly, *J. Physiol.* **121**, 31P.

Andrew, A.M. & Roberts, T.D.M. (1954) A pulse-interval meter for measuring pulse repetition frequency, *Electronic Engg.* **26**, 469–474 and 543–547.

Apter, J.T. (1945) Projection of the retina on the superior colliculus of the cat *J. Neurophysiol.* **8**, 123.

Arbib, M.A. (1970) Cognition – a Cybernetics approach. In: Garvin, P.L. (ed.) *Cognition, A Multiple View*, Spartan, N.Y., pp. 331–384.

Arbib, M.A. (1977) Book review, *Bull. Amer. Math. Soc.* **83**, 946–951.

Ashby, W.R. (1956) *An Introduction to Cybernetics*, Wiley, N.Y.

Ashby, W.R. (1960) *Design for a Brain*, 2nd edn., Chapman & Hall London.

Ashby, W.R. (1964) The next ten years. In: Tou, J.T. & Wilcox, R.H. (eds) *Computer and Information Sciences*, Spartan, Washington, pp. 2–11.

Ashby, W.R. (1967) The set theory of mechanism and homeostasis. In: Stewart, D.J. (ed.), *Automaton Theory and Learning Systems*, Academic Press, London, pp. 23–51.

Banerji, R.B. (1969) *Theory of problem Solving*, Elsevier, N.Y.

Barto, A.G., Sutton, R.S. & Brouwer, P.S. (1980) *Associative Search Network: A Reinforcement Learning Associative Memory*, COINS Technical Report 80-18, Univ. of Massachusetts, Amherst.

Bellman, K.L. & Goldberg, L.J. (1984) Common origin of linguistic and movement abilities *Am. J. Physiol.* **246** (*Regulatory Integrative Comp. Physiol.* **15**), R915–R921.

Bellman, R. (1961) *Adaptive Control Processes: A Guided Tour*, Princeton Univ. Press, Princeton, N.J.

Bellman, R. (1964) Dynamic programming, learning, and adaptive processing. In: Tou, J.T. & Wilcox, R.H. (eds) *Computer and Information Sciences*, Spartan, Washington, pp. 375–380.

Berliner, H.J. (1985) Multiprocessing and duality in intelligence. In: Steels, L. & Campbell, J.A. (eds) *Progress in Artificial Intelligence*, Ellis Horwood, Chichester, pp. 112–128.

Birkhoff, G. & MacLane, S. (1953) *A Survey of Modern Algebra*, (revised edition) Macmillan, N.Y.

Bobrow, D.G. (1968) Natural language input for a computer problem-solving system. In: Minsky, M. (ed.) *Semantic Information Processing*, MIT Press, Cambridge, Mass., Ch. 3.

Bobrow, D.G. (1984) Qualitative reasoning about physical systems, *Artificial Intelligence* **24**, 1–5.

Borovac, B., Vukobratović, M. & Surla, D. (1989) An approach to biped control synthesis, *Robotica* **7**, 231–241.

Box, M.J. (1965) A new method of constrained optimization and a comparison with other methods, *Computer Jnl.* **8**, 42–52.

Boyd, I.A. & Roberts, T.D.M. (1953) Proprioceptive discharges from stretch-receptors in the knee-joint of the cat, *J. Physiol.* **122**, 38–58.

Brady, J.M. (ed.) (1981) *Computer Vision*, North-Holland, Amsterdam.

Bruner, J.S., Goodnow, J.J. & Austin, G.A. (1956) *A Study of Thinking*, Wiley, N.Y.

Buchanan, B.G. (1982) New research on expert systems. In: Hayes, J.E., Michie, D. & Pao, Y.-H. (eds) *Machine Intelligence 10*, Ellis Horwood, Chichester, pp. 269–299.

Carbonell, J.G. (1984) Learning by analogy: formulating and generalizing plans from past experience. In: Michalski, R.S., Carbonell, J.G. & Mitchell, T.M. (eds) *Machine Learning*, Springer, Berlin, pp. 137–161.

Chouraqui, E. (1985) Construction of a model for reasoning by analogy. In: Steels, L. & Campbell, J.A. (eds) *Progress in Artificial Intelligence*, Ellis Horwood, Chichester, pp. 169–183.

Churchland, P.S. (1986) *Neurophilosophy–Toward a Unified Science of the Mind/Brain*, MIT Press, Cambridge, Mass.

Collins, J.S. (1967) A regression analysis program incorporating heuristic term selection. In: Dale, E. & Michie, D. (eds) *Machine Intelligence 2*, Oliver & Boyd, Edinburgh, pp. 153–170.

Craggs, J.W. (1963) *Calculus of Variations*, Allen and Unwin, London.

Darwin, C. (1897) *The Formation of Vegetable Mould through the Action of Worms*, John Murray, London.

de Bono (1970) *The Dog-Exercising Machine*, Jonathan Cape, London.

de Kleer, J. (1984) How circuits work, *Artificial Intelligence* **24**, 205–280.

de Kleer, J. & Brown, J.S. (1984) A qualitative physics based on confluences, *Artificial Intelligence* **24**, 7–83.

Delgado, A.E., Mira, J. & Moreno-Diaz, R. (1989) A neurocybernetic model of modal cooperative decisions in the Kilmer-McCulloch space, *Kybernetes* **18**, 48–57.

Donaldson, P.E.K. (1960) Error decorrelation: a technique for matching a class of functions. *Proc. 3rd Conf. on Medical Electronics*, London, p. 173.

Donaldson, P.E.K. (1964) Error decorrelation studies on a human operator performing a balancing task, *Medical Electronics and Biological Engineering* **2**, 393–410.

Draper, N. & Smith, H. (1966) *Applied Regression Analysis*, Wiley, N.Y.

Dreyfus, H.L. (1965) *Alchemy and Artificial Intelligence*, Report P-3244, Rand Corporation, Santa Monica.

Eigen, M. & Schuster, P. (1977) The Hypercycle, a principle of natural self-organization, *Naturwissenschaften* **64**, 541–565, **65**, 7–41 & 341–369.

Elkind, D. & Flavell, J.H. (eds) (1969) *Studies in Cognitive Development: Essays in Honor of Jean Piaget*, O.U.P., N.Y.

Elmaghraby, A.S., Jagannathan, V. & Ralston, P. (1985) An expert system for process control. In: Holmes, W.M. (ed.) *Artificial Intelligence and Simulation*, Soc. for Computer Simulation, San Diego.

Evans, C.L. (1949) *Principles of Human Physiology*, Churchill, London, p. 306.

Everitt, B. (1974) *Cluster Analysis*. Heinemann, London.

Feigenbaum, E.A. & Feldman, J. (eds) (1963) *Computers and Thought*, McGraw-Hill, N.Y.

Fischler, M.A. & Firschein, O. (1987) *Intelligence: The Eye, the Brain, and the Computer*, Addison-Wesley, Reading, Mass.

Fish, A.N. (1981) *The Conformon: A Synaptic Model of Learning*, Ph.D. Thesis, Dept. of Psychology, Univ. of Manchester.

Fogel, L.J., Owens, A.J. & Walsh, M.J. (1966) *Artificial Intelligence through Simulated Evolution*, Wiley, N.Y.

Forsyth, R. (1981) Beagle – a Darwinian approach to pattern recognition, *Kybernetes* **10**, 3, 159–166.

Forsyth, R. & Naylor, C. (1985) *The Hitch-Hiker's Guide to Artificial Intelligence*, Chapman & Hall, London.

Forsyth, R. & Rada, R. (1986) *Machine Learning Applications in Expert Systems and Information Retrieval*, Ellis Horwood, Chichester.

Foulkes, J.D. (1959) A class of machines which determines statistical structure of a sequence of characters. In: *IRE Wescon Convention Record*, pt. 4, 66–73.

Freeman, W.J. (1986) W. Grey Walter: The Living Brain. In: Palm, G. & Aerten, A. (eds), *Brain Theory*, Springer, Berlin, pp. 237–238.

Freund, E. & Hoyer, H. (1988) Real-time pathfinding in multirobot systems including obstacle avoidance, *Int. J. Robotics Research* **7**, 42–70.

Friedberg, R.M. (1958) A learning machine, part 1, *IBM Jnl. Res. and Dev.* **2**, 2–13.

Friedberg, R.M., Dunham, B. & North, J.H. (1959) A learning machine, part 2, *IBM Jnl. Res. and Dev.* **3**, 822–287.

Fulton, J.F. (1949) *Physiology of the Nervous System*, O.U.P., N.Y.

Gabor, D. (1954) Communication theory and cybernetics, *Trans. I.R.E.* **CT-1**, 4, 19.

Gabor, D. (1968a) Holographic model of temporal recall, *Nature* **217**, 584.

Gabor, D. (1968b) Improved holographic model of temporal recall, *Nature* **217**, 1288–1289.

Gabor, D., Wilby, W.P.L. & Woodcock, R. (1961), A universal non-linear filter, predictor and simulator which optimizes itself by a learning process, *Proc. I.E.E. (London)* **B 13**, 422–435.

Gaines, B.R. (1977) System identification, approximation and complexity, *Int. J. General Systems* **3**, 145–174.

Galopin, G.C. (1989) A unified concept of the ecological niche, *Int. J. General Systems* **15**, 59–73.

Gaze, R.M. (1970) *The Formulation of Nerve Connections*, Academic Press, N.Y.

Gaze, R.M. & Jacobson, M. (1963) 'Convexity-detectors' in the frog visual system, *J. Physiol.* **169**, 1P–3P.

Genesereth, M.R. & Nilsson, N.J. (1987) *Logical Foundations of Artificial Intelligence*, Morgan Kaufmann, Los Altos.

George, F.H. (1973) *The Brain as a Computer* 2nd edn., Pergamon, Oxford, p. 128.

George, F.H. (1976) *Precision, Language and Logic*, Pergamon, Oxford, p. 183.

George, F. & Johnson, L. (eds) (1985) *Purposive Behaviour and Teleological Explanations*, Gordon and Breach, N.Y.

George, F.H. & Humphries, J.D. (eds) (1974) *The Robots are Coming*, N.C.C. Publications, Manchester.

Gerardy, R. (1989) New methods for the identification of finite state systems, *Int. J. General Systems* **15**, 97–112.

Ginsberg, M.L. (1985) Does probability have a place in nonmonotonic reasoning? *Proc. Ninth IJCAI*, 107–110.

Ginsberg, M.L. (ed.) (1987) *Readings in Nonmonotonic Reasoning*, Morgan Kaufmann, Los Altos.

Glushkov, V.M. (1966) *Introduction to Cybernetics*, Academic Press, N.Y.

Good, I.J. (1965) The mystery of GO, *New Scientist*, No. 427, 172–174.

Hall, R.P. (1989) Computational approaches to analogical reasoning: a comparative analysis, *Artificial Intelligence* **39**, 39–120.

Hamdi, P.A. & Whitteridge, D. (1953) The representation of the retina on the optic lobe of the pigeon and the superior colliculus of the rabbit and the goat, *J. Physiol.* **121**, 44P.

Harth, E.M., Csermely, T.J., Beek, R. & Lindsay, R.D. (1970) Brain functions and neural dynamics, *J. Theor. Biol* **26**, 93–120.

Hebb, D.O. (1961) *Organization of Behaviour*, Science Editions, N.Y.

Hebb, D.O. (1980) *Essay on Mind*, Lawrence Erlbaum, Hillsdale, New Jersey.

Hemami, H. & Zheng, Y.-F. (1984) Dynamics and control of motion on the ground and in the air with application to biped robots, *J. Robotic Systems* **1**, 1, 101–116.

Hinton, G.E. (1989) Connectionist learning procedures, *Artificial Intelligence* **40**, 185–234.

Hofstadter, D.R. (1980) *Gödel, Escher, Bach: An Eternal Golden Braid*, Penguin Books, London, p. 18.

Hopfield, J.J. (1982) Neural networks and physical systems with emergent collective computational properties, *Proc. Natl. Acad. Sci. USA* **79**, 2554–2558.

Hoyle, F. & Wickramasinghe, C. (1980) *The Origin of Life*. Univ. Coll. Cardiff Press, Cardiff.

Hubel, D.H. & Wiesel, T.N. (1962) Receptive fields, binocular interaction and functional architecture in the cat's visual cortex, *J. Physiol.* **160**, 106–154.

Hubel, D.H. & Wiesel, T.N. (1968) Receptive fields and functional architecture of monkey striate cortex, *J. Physiol.* **195**, 215–243.

Hunt, E.B., Marin, J. & Stone, P.J. (1966) *Experiments in Induction*, Academic Press, N.Y.

IFAC (1961) *Automatic and Remote Control*, IFAC Moscow Congress), Butterworth, London.

Jantsch, E. (1980) *The Self-Organizing Universe*, Pergamon, Oxford.

Kalman, R.E. (1958) Design of a self-optimizing control system, *Trans. A.S.M.E.*, Feb., 468.

Kanal, L.N., Levitt, T.S. & Lemmer, J.F. (eds) (1989) *Uncertainty in Artificial Intelligence* **3**, North-Holland, Amsterdam.

Kanerva, P. (1988) *Sparse Distributed Memory*, MIT Press, Cambridge, Mass.

Kapur, D. & Mundy, J.L. (eds) (1989) *Geometric Reasoning*, MIT Press, Cambridge, Mass.

Khatib, O. (1986) Real-time obstacle avoidance for manipulators and mobile robots, *Int. J. Robotics Research* **5**, 90–98.

Kilmer, W.L., McCulloch, W.S. & Blum, J. (1968) Some mechanisms for a theory of the reticular formation. In: Mesarovic, M.D. (ed;) *Systems Theory and Biology*, Springer, N.Y., p. 286.

Kilmer, W.L., McCulloch, W.S. & Blum, J. (1969) A model of the vertebrate central command system, *Int. J. Man-Machine Studies* **1**, 279–309.

Klir, G.J. (1985) Complexity: some general observations, *Systems Research* **2**, 2, 131–140.

Klir, G.J. (1988) Multidimensional information theory and general systems methodology. In: Trappl, R. (ed.) *Cybernetics and Systems '88*, Kluwer, Dordrecht, pp. 3–10.

Klir, G.J. (1989) Is there more to uncertainty than some probability theorists might have us believe? *Int. J. General Systems* **15**, 347–378.

Klir, G.J. & Folger, T.A. (1988) *Fuzzy Sets, Uncertainty, and Information*, Prentice-Hall, Englewood Cliffs, N.J.

Kochen, M. (1981) Appropriate approximation in concept genesis. In: Lasker, G.E. (ed.) *Applied Systems and Cybernetics*, Pergamon, N.Y., pp. 613–618.

Landahl, H.D., McCulloch, W.S. & Pitts, W. (1943) A statistical consequence of the logical calculus of nervous nets. *Bull. Math. Biophysics* **5**, 135–137.

Lehmann, E.L. (1975) *Nonparametrics: Statistical Methods Based on Ranks*, Holden-Day, San Francisco.

Lenat, D.B. (1984) The role of heuristics in learning by discovery – three case studies. In: Michalski, R.S., Carbonell, J.G. & Mitchell, T.M. (eds), *Machine Learning*, Springer, Berlin, pp. 343 – 306.

Lettvin, J.Y., Maturana, H.R., McCulloch, W.S. & Pitts, W. (1959) What the frog's eye tells the frog's brain, *Proc. I.R.E.* **47**, 1940-1951.

Longuet-Higgins, H.C. (1968) Holographic model of temporal recall, *Nature* **217**, 104.

Lovelock J.E. (1979) *Gaia: A New Look at Life on Earth*, University Press, Oxford.

Lovelock J.E. (1981) More on Gaia and the end of Gaia, *CoEvolution Quarterly*, No. 31, Fall 1981, 34 – 37.

Lovelock J.E. (1983) Gaia as seen through the atmosphere. In: Westbroek, P. & de Jong, E.W. (eds) *Biomineralization and Biological Metal Accumulation*, Reidel, Dordrecht, pp. 15 – 25.

Lovelock J.E. (1986) Gaia: the world as living organism, *New Scientist* **18**, December, 25 – 28.

Lubbock, J.K. (1961) A self-optimizing non-linear filter *Proc. I.E.E. (London)* **B 13**, 439 – 440.

Luce, R.D. & Raiffa, H. (1957) *Games and Decisions*, Wiley, N.Y.

MacKay, D.M. (1959) On the combination of digital and analogue techniques in the design of analytical engines. In: *Mechanisation of Thought Processes*. H.M.S.O., London, 55 – 65.

Malsburg, Ch. von der (1986) Frank Rosenblatt: Principles of Neurodynamics. In: Palm, G. & Aerten, A. (eds), *Brain Theory*, Springer, Berlin, pp. 245 – 248.

Marr, D. (1969) A theory for cerebellar cortex, *J. Physiol.* **202**, 437 – 470.

Marr, D. (1970) A theory of cerebral neocortex, *Proc. Roy. Soc. (Lond.)* **B176**, 161 – 234.

Marr, D. (1971) Simple memory: a theory for archicortex, *Phil. Trans. Roy. Soc. (Lond.)* **B262**, 23 – 81.

Marr, D. (1976) Early processing of visual information, *Phil. Trans. Roy. Soc. (Lond.)* **B275**, 483 – 524.

Marr, D. (1982) *Vision*, Freeman, San Francisco.

Maturana, H.R. (1975) The organization of the living: a theory of the living organization, *Int. Jnl. Man-Machine Studies* **7**, 313 – 332.

McCarthy, J. (1980) Circumscription–a form of nonmonotonic reasoning, *Artificial Intelligence* **13**, 27–39. Reprinted in: Ginsberg, M.L. (ed.) (1987) *Readings in Nonmonotonic Reasoning*, Morgan Kaufmann, Los Altos, pp. 145–152.

McCorduck, P. (1979) *Machines Who Think*, Freeman, San Francisco.

McCulloch, W.S. (1959) Agatha Tyche: Of nervous nets–the lucky reckoners. In: *Mechanisation of Thought Processes*, H.M.S.O., London, pp. 611–633.

McCulloch, W.S. (1960) What is a number, that a man may know it, and a man, that he may know a number? *General Semantics Bulletin*, nos. 26 & 27, 7–18.

McCulloch, W.S. (1974) Recollections of the many sources of Cybernetics, *A.S.C. Forum* **4**, no. 2, 5–16.

McCulloch, W.S. & Pitts, W (1943) A logical calculus of the ideas immanent in nervous activity, *Bull. Math. Biophysics* **5**, 115–133.

Minsky, M.L. (1959a) Some methods of artificial intelligence and heuristic programming. In: *Mechanisation of Thought Processes*, H.M.S.O., London, pp. 3–36.

Minsky, M. (1959b) Contribution to discussion. In: *Mechanisation of Thought Processes*, H.M.S.O., London, p. 71.

Minsky, M. (1963) Steps towards artificial intelligence . In: Feigenbaum, E.A. & Feldman, J. (eds) *Computers and Thought*, McGraw-Hill, N.Y., pp. 406–450.

Minsky, M.L. (1967) *Finite and Infinite Machines*, Prentice-Hall, Englewood Cliffs, New Jersey.

Minsky, M. & Papert, S. (1969) *Perceptrons*, MIT Press, Cambridge, Mass.

Minsky, M. & Selfridge, O.G. (1961) Learning in random nets. In: Cherry, E.C, (ed.) *Information Theory*, Butterworth, London, pp. 335–347.

Moore, W. (1989) *Schrödinger: Life and thought*, University Press, Cambridge.

Morecki, A., Ekiel, J. & Fidelus, K. (1984) *Cybernetic Systems of Limb Movements in Man, Animals and Robots*, Ellis Horwood, Chichester.

Newell, A., Shaw, J.C. & Simon, H. (1959) Report on a general problem-solving program. In: *Proc. Int. Conf. on Information Processing*, UNESCO, Paris, pp. 256–264.

Newell, A., Shaw, J.C. & Simon, H. (1960) A variety of intelligent learning in a general problem solver. In: Yovits, M. & Cameron, S. (eds) *Self-Organizing Systems*, Pergamon, N.Y., pp. 153–189.

Newell, A. & Simon, H. (1963) GPS, a program that simulates human thought. In: Feigenbaum, E.A. & Feldman, J. (eds) *Computers and Thought*, McGraw-Hill, N.Y., pp. 279–293.

Nilsson, N.J. (1965) *Learning Machines*, McGraw-Hill, N.Y.

Parks, J.R. (1969) A multi-level system of analysis for mixedfont and hand-blocked printed characters recognition. In: Grasselli, A. (ed), *Automatic Interpretation and Classsification of Images*, Academic Press, N.Y., pp. 395–322.

Pask, G. (1959) Physical analogues to the growth of a concept.   In: *Mechanisation of Thought Processes*, H.M.S.O., London, pp. 877–928.

Pask, A.G. (1961a) Contribution to discussion, *Proc. I.E.E. (London)* **B13**, p. 437.

Pask, Gordon (1961b) *An Approach to Cybernetics*, Hutchinson, London.

Pask, G. (1962) The logical type of illogical evolution.   In: *Information Processing* (Proceedings of IFIP Congress), North-Holland, Amsterdam. p. 482.

Pask, G. (1975) *Conversation, Cognition and Learning*, Elsevier, Amsterdam.

Paynter, H.M. (1960) *Analysis and Design of Engineering Systems*, MIT Press, Cambridge. Mass.

Pearl, J. (1984) *Heuristics: Intelligent Search Strategies for Computer Problem Solving*, Addison-Wesley, Reading, Mass.

Pedrycz, W. (1989) *Fuzzy Control and Fuzzy Systems*, Research Studies, Taunton, and Wiley, N.Y.

Pellionisz, A.J. (1986) Tensor network theory of the central nervous system and sensorimotor modeling. In: Palm, G. & Aerton, A. (eds) *Brain Theory*, Springer, Berlin, pp. 121–145.

Pellionisz, A.J. (1988) Vistas from tensor network theory: a horizon from reductionalistic neurophilosphy to the geometry of multi-unit recordings. In: Cotterill, R.M.J. (ed) *Computer Simulation in Brain Science*, University Press, Cambridge, pp. 44–73.

Penfield, W. & Rasmussen, T. (1950) *The Cerebral Cortex of Man*, Macmillan, N.Y.

Philbrick, G.A. (1960) *Continuous Electric Representation of Non-Linear Functions of n Variables: A Palimpsest on the Electronic Analog Art*, George A. Philbrick Reserches Inc., Cambridge, Mass.

Polya, G. (1954) *Mathematics and Plausible Reasoning* (2 vols.), University Press, Princeton.

Polya, G. (1957) *How to Solve It: A New Aspect of Mathematical Method*, 2nd edn., Doubleday Anchor, N.Y.

Pontryagin, L.S., Boltyanskii, V.G., Gamkrelidze, R.V. & Mishchenko, E.F. (1963) *The Mathematical Theory of Optimal Processes*, Interscience, N.Y.

Powell, M.J.D. (1968) On the calculation of orthogonal vectors, *Computer Jnl.* **11**, 302–304.

Prigogine, I. (1971) Unity of physical laws and levels of description. In: Grene, M. (ed.), *Interpretations of Life and Mind*, Humanities Presse, N.Y., pp. 1–13.

Prigogine, I. & Stengers, I. (1884) *Order out of Chaos: Man's New Dialogue with Nature*, Fontana, London.

Raibert, M.H. (1984) Introduction to special issue on legged locomotion, *Int. J. Robotics Research* **3**, 2, 2–3.

Raibert, M.H. (1985) *Legged Robots that Balance*, MIT Press, Cambridge, Mass.

Ralston, A. & Rabinowitz, P. (1978) *A First Course in Numerical Analysis*, 2nd edn., McGraw-Hill International.

Raphael, B. (1968) SIR: A computer program for semantic information retrieval. In: Minsky, M. (ed) *Semantic Information Processing*, MIT Press, Cambridge, Mass.

Rich, E. (1983) *Artificial Intelligence*, McGraw-Hill, N.Y.

Roberts, L.G. (1960) Pattern recognition with an adaptive network. In: *IRE Intl. Conv. Record*, pt. 2, 66–70.

Robinson, J.A. (1965) A machine-oriented logic based on the resolution principle, *J. A.C.M.* **12**, 23–41.

Rosen, R. (1985) *Anticipatory Systems*, Pergamon, Oxford.

Rosenblatt, F, (1959) Two theorems of statistical separability in the perceptron. In: *Mechanisation of Thought Processes*, H.M.S.O., London, pp. 421–456.

Rosenblatt, F, (1961) *Principles of Neurodynamics*, Spartan Books, N.Y.

Rosenbrock, H.H. (1960) An automatic method for finding the greatest or least value of a function, *Computer Jnl.* **3**, 175–184.

Roska, T. (1988) Analog events and a dual computing structure using analog and digital circuits and operators. In: Varaiya, P. & Kurzhanski, A.B. (eds) *Discrete Event Systems: Models and Applications*, Springer, Berlin, pp. 225–238.

Rothenberg, D. (1975) Predicate calculus feature generation. In: Storer, T. & Winter, D. (eds), *Formal Aspects of Cognitive Processes*, Springer, Berlin, pp. 72–125.

Rumelhart, D.E., McClelland, J.L. *et al* (1986) *Parallel Distributed Processing* (2 vols.), MIT Press, Cambridge, Mass.

Samuel, A.L. (1963) Some studies in machine learning using the game of checkers. In: Feigenbaum, E.A. & Feldman, J. (eds) *Computers and Thought*, McGraw-Hill, N.Y., pp. 71–105.

Schank, R.C. (1985) Looking at learning. In: Steels, L. & Campbell, J.A. (eds), *Progress in Artificial Intelligence*, Ellis Horwood, Chichester, pp. 17–29.

Schwartz, J.T. & Sharir, M. (1989) A survey of motion planning and related geometric algorithms. In: Kapur, D. & Mundy, J.L. (eds) *Geometric Reasoning*, MIT Press, Cambridge, Mass., pp. 157–169.

Schwefel, H.-P (1981) *Numerical Optimization of Computer Models*, Wiley, Chichester.

Science Research Council (1973) *Artificial Intelligence: a paper symposium.*

Searle, J. (1984) *Minds, Brains and Science* (The 1984 Reith Lectures), British Broadcasting Corporation, London.

Sejnowski, T.J. (1986) Open questions about computation in cerebral cortex. In: Rumelhart, D.E., McClelland, J.L. *et al* (1986) *Parallel Distributed Processing* (2 vols.), MIT Press, Cambridge, Mass., pp. 372–389.

Selfridge, O.G. (1956) Pattern recognition and learning. In: Cherry, E.C. (ed.) *Information Theory*, Butterwporth, London, p. 345.

Selfridge, O.G. (1959) Pandemonium: a paradigm for learning. In: *Mechanisation of Thought Processes*, H.M.S.O., London, pp. 511–531.

Selfridge, O.G. & Neisser, U. (1963) Pattern recognition by machine. In: Feigenbaum, E.A. & Feldman, J. (eds) *Computers and Thought*, McGraw-Hill, N.Y., pp. 237–250.

Shannon, C.E. & Weaver, W. (1949) *The Mathematical theory of Communication*, Univ. of Illinois Press, Urbana.

Slagle, J.R. (1963) A heuristic program that solves symbolic integration problems in freshman calculus. In: Feigenbaum, E.A. & Feldman, J. (eds) *Computers and Thought*, McGraw-Hill, N.Y., pp. 191–203.

Slagle, J.R. (1971) *Artificial Intelligence: The Heuristic Programming Approach*, McGraw-Hill, N.Y.

Sommerhoff, G. (1950) *Analytical Biology*, Oxford University Press.

Sommerhoff, G. (1974) *Logic of the Living Brain*, Wiley, London.

Sorenson, H.W. (1985) (ed.) *Kalman Filtering: Theory and Application*, IEEE Press, N.Y.

Sowan, F. & Horwood, E. (1987) *Publishing with Ellis Horwood* 2nd edn., Ellis Horwood, Chichester.

Steinbuch, K. (1961) Die Lernmatrix, *Kybernetik* 1, 36–45.

Steinbuch, K. & Piske, U.A.W. (1963) Learning matrices and their applications, *IEEE Trans.* EC-12, 846–682.

Strachey, C. (1959) Contribution to discussion. In: *Mechanisation of Thought Processes*, H.M.S.O., London, pp. 507–508.

Szentágothai, J. & Arbib, M.A. (1976) *Conceptual Models of Neural Organization*, MIT Press, Cambridge, Mass.

Szolovits, P. & Pauker, S.G. (1984) Categorical and probabilistic reasoning in medical diagnosis. In: Clancey, W.J. & Shortliffe, E.H. (eds) *Readings in Medical Artificial Intelligence*, Addison-Wesley, Reading, Mass., pp. 210–240.

Troch, I. (1989a) Time-optimal path generation for continuous and quasi-continuous path control of industrial robots, *J. Intelligent and Robotic Systems* **2**. 1–28.

Troch, I. (1989b) Time-suboptimal quasi-continuous path generation for industrial robots, *Robotica* **7**, 297–302.

Uttley, A.M. (1956) A theory of the mechanism of learning based on the computation of conditional probabilities, *Proc. First Int. Conι;·‹·‹› of Cybernetics, Namur*, Gauthier-Villars, Paris, pp. 830–856.

Uttley, A.M. (1959) Conditional probability computing in a nervous system. In: *Mechanisation of Thought Processes*, H.M.S.O., London, pp. 119–147.

Visser, H. & Molenaar, J. (1988) Kalman filter analysis in dendroclimatology, *Biometrics* **44**, 929–940.

von Mises, R. (1939) *Probability, Statistics and Truth*, William Hodge, London.

Wall, P.D. & Egger, M.D. (1971) Formation of new connections in adult rat brains after partial deafferentation, *Nature* **232**, 542–545.

Wall, P.D., Fitzgerald,, M. & Woolf, C.J. (1982) Effects of capsaicin on receptive fields and on inhibitors in rat spinal cord, *Exptl. Neurology* **78**, 425–436.

Wallace, G.K. (1989) The control of oscillatory movements of the forearm, *Biol. Cybern.* **61**, 233–240.

Walter, W. Grey (1953) *The Living Brain*, Duckworth, London, pp. 203–207.

Warwick, K. & Pugh, A. (eds) (1988) *Robot Control: Theory and Applications*, Peter Peregrinus, London, on behalf of IEE, London.

Watson, A.J. & Lovelock, J.E. (1983) Biological homeostasis of the global environment: the parable of Daisyworld, *Tellus 35B*, pp. 284–289.

Weir, M. (1984) *Goal-Directed Behaviour*, Gordon & Breach, N.Y.

Wiener, N. (1948) *Cybernetics*, Wiley, N.Y., p. 150.

Wilson, H.R. & Cowan, J.D. (1972) Excitatory and inhibitory interactions in localized populations of model neurons, *Biophysical Journal* **12**, 1–24.

Winograd, T. (1973) *Understanding Natural Language*, Edinburgh Univ. Press, Edinburgh.

Winston, P.S. (1975) Learning structural description from examples.   In: Winston, P.S. (ed.) *The Psychology of Computer Vision*, McGraw-Hill, N.Y.

Winston, P.S. (1980) Learning and reasoning by analogy, *Comm. A.C.M.* **23**, 689–703.

Winston, P.S. (1984) *Machine Intelligence*, 2nd edn., Addison-Wesley, Reading, Mass., Ch 12.

Witten, I.H. (1978) Exploring, modelling and controlling discrete sequential environments. In: Klir, G.J. (ed.) *Applied General Systems Research*, Plenum, N.Y., pp. 161–174.

Witten, I.H. (1979) Approximate non-deterministic modelling of behaviour sequences, *Int. J. General Systems* **5**, 1–12.

Wylie, C.R. & Barrett, L.C. (1982) *Advanced Engineering Mathematics*, 5th edn., McGraw-Hill International.

Yevin, I.A. & Yablonsky, A.I. (1985) Models of development and the catastrophe theory. In: Gvishiani, J.M. (ed.) *System Research 2: Methodological Problems*, Pergamon, Oxford, pp. 159–181.

Zadeh, L.A. (1965) Fuzzy sets, *Information and Control* **8**. 338–353.

Zadeh, L.A. (1983) The role of fuzzy logic in the management of uncertainty in expert systems, *Fuzzy Sets and Systems* **11**, 199–227.

Appendix A   Pascal Programs

A.1 MAIN OPTIMIZATION PROGRAM

The main program embodying Rosenbrock's method is as follows, except for the insertions from other files indicated by the pseudo-comments {$I B:SIXEVAL.PAS} and {$I B:EXAMINE.PAS}.

```
PROGRAM rosenbrock(input, output);
   {This implements the method for up to 17 dimensions, with
   modifications to adapt it to the trajectory problem}

CONST pi= 3.14159265359;

TYPE vec= ARRAY[1..17] OF real;
     mat= ARRAY[1..17,1..17] OF real;
     evaln= RECORD   reach: integer;
                     miss: real;
                     tim: real;
                     success: boolean  END;
        {The objective function is of TYPE evaln - see text}

VAR   alpha, beta, b: real;
         {"alpha", "beta" are multipliers for step length in
         the optimization.   "b" is the damping coefficient}
      display, dispmem, interact, publish,
         guillotine, repoint, fixa, filestart,
         reorigin, done: boolean;
            {"display", "dispmem" refer to graphic display,
            "interact" to facility for manual alteration,
            "publish" to writing on results file,
            "guillotine" to limiting trials in a stage;
            "repoint" means reorientation is effective,
            "fixa" means acceleration "a" not variable,
            "filestart" means initial settings from file}
```

Continued overleaf

141

```
        evalcnt, evalint, recordint,
          maxreach, effvars, maxstage: integer;
            {"evalcnt" is a count of evaluations, and the
            next two are intervals between tabulations of
            values, on screen and in the record file,
            respectively.
            "maxreach" refers to max travel achieved,
            "effvars" to effective no. of variables, and
            "maxstage" to trials allowed by "guillotine"}

        filename: string;
        results, manstart: text;

FUNCTION gteq(x, y: evaln): boolean;
  {Compares objects of TYPE evaln}
BEGIN  IF x.reach <> y.reach THEN
           gteq:= x.reach > y.reach
    ELSE IF x.miss <> y.miss THEN
           gteq:= x.miss < y.miss
    ELSE  gteq:= x.tim <= y.tim
END {gteq};

FUNCTION ask(prompt:string): boolean;
  {Allows manual setting of booleans}
VAR ch: char;
BEGIN  ch:=' ';  WHILE NOT ((ch='Y') OR (ch='y')
  OR (ch='N') OR (ch='n')) DO
  BEGIN writeln(prompt);   readln(ch);
    ask:= (ch='Y') OR (ch ='y')
  END
END {ask};

PROCEDURE orth(prog: vec;  VAR dir: mat;
                   VAR b1, b2: real;  n: integer);
  {This carries out the Gram-Schmidt orthogonalization
  method, on the upper left (nxn) square within "dir",
  where "prog" holds the progress in each of the n
  directions in the previous stage.  "b1" and "b2" are
  evaluated for interest, and refer to a stopping rule
  suggested by Rosenbrock}
```

Continued opposite

```
VAR   a: mat;
      i, ii, j: integer;
      x: real;
BEGIN   FOR i:= 1 TO n DO   FOR j:= 1 TO n DO
                                          a[i, j]:= 0;
  FOR j:= 1 TO n DO a[n, j]:= prog[n]*dir[n, j];
  FOR i:= n-1 DOWNTO 1 DO   FOR j:= 1 TO n DO
    a[i, j]:= a[i+1, j] + prog[i]*dir[i, j];
    {"a" now represents the progress in the previous
    stage, represented as vectors according to
    original coordinates.  Row 1 represents total
    progress, row 2 progress in all except first
    direction, row 3 progress in all except first 2
    directions, and so on}
  FOR i:= 1 TO n DO
  BEGIN   FOR j:= 1 TO n DO dir[i, j]:= a[i, j];
      {i-th row of "dir" becomes copy of i-th of "a"}
    FOR ii:= 1 TO i-1 DO
    BEGIN   x:= 0;
      FOR j:= 1 TO n DO x:= x+a[i, j]*dir[ii, j];
      FOR j:= 1 TO n DO
            dir[i, j]:= dir[i, j]-x*dir[ii, j]
    END;
      {i-th row of "dir" has subtracted from it the
      projection onto it of each previous direction}
    x:= 0;
    FOR j:= 1 TO n DO x:= x+sqr(dir[i, j]);
    x:= sqrt(x);
    FOR j:= 1 TO n DO dir[i, j]:= dir[i, j]/x
      {i-th row of "dir" is normalised to be a unit
      vector}
  END;
  x:= 0;   FOR j:= 1 TO n DO x:= x+sqr(a[1, j]);
  b1:= sqrt(x);
  x:= 0;   FOR j:= 1 TO n DO x:= x+sqr(a[2, j]);
  b2:= sqrt(x)
      {Rosenbrock's criteria "b1", "b2" are evaluated}
END {orth};
```

Continued overleaf

```
{$I B:SIXEVAL.PAS}
{This is a non-standard instruction to insert material here
from a source file called SIXEVAL.  It supplies the
procedure "eval", called as a parameter of procedure
"rose"}

PROCEDURE rose(n, nstages: integer;
        PROCEDURE obj(x: vec; st,tr: integer; VAR u:evaln));
  {This implements Rosenbrock's method, in up to "n"
  dimensions (n <= 17), and up to "nstage" stages.  The
  procedure "obj" evaluates the objective function, as
  its parameter "u", on the basis of vector "x".
  The stage and trial nos. are also represented, purely for
  use in "display"}
LABEL 1, 999;
VAR  x, x1, step, prog: vec;
  {"x" is current operating point, and "x1" a trial
  displacment.  "u" and "u1" hold evaluations.
  "step" holds step lengths, and "prog" total progress}
    dir: mat;
    succ, fail: ARRAY[1..17] OF boolean;
      {Entries become true when success of failure
      occurs for move in corresponding direction}
    i, j, k, stage, trial: integer;
    b1, b2: real;
    u, u1: evaln;
    endstage: boolean;

PROCEDURE origin;
  {This resets "succ", "fail", "prog"}
  VAR i: integer;
  BEGIN  FOR i:=1 TO n DO
    BEGIN  prog[i]:= 0;  succ[i]:= false;  fail[i]:= false
    END   END {origin};

PROCEDURE showval;   {Show values on screen}
VAR i: integer;
  BEGIN  writeln(output);  writeln(output);
      FOR i:=1 TO n DO
      BEGIN  write('(',i:2,') ',x[i]:7);
        IF (i=n) OR ((i MOD 5)=0) THEN writeln(output)
            ELSE write('  ')
```

Continued opposite

```
        END;  writeln(output)
END {showval};

PROCEDURE stow;  {Record values in file "results"}
VAR i, j: integer;
BEGIN
  writeln(results,'Stage', stage:3, ' Trials', trial:5,
                ' Evalns.', evalcnt:5);
  writeln(results,'Objective fn.', u.reach:3, u.miss:5,
                                              u.tim:5);
        writeln(results,'Variables:');
        FOR j:= 1 TO n DO
        IF (j MOD 6 = 0) OR (j=n) THEN writeln(results,x[j]:9)
          ELSE write(results,x[j]:9);
        writeln(results)
END {stow};

{$I B:EXAMINE.PAS}
{This  inserts a procedure "examine", not reproduced here,
to allow manual interaction with the process}

BEGIN
  FOR i:= 1 TO n DO x[i]:= 0;
  IF fixa THEN x[n]:=1 ELSE x[1]:=1;
      {If "a" is fixed it becomes variable no. 17, otherwise
      it is no. 1.  This allows "orth" to work on an
      appropriate subset of variables}
  IF filestart THEN
  BEGIN  IF fixa THEN
    BEGIN read(manstart,x[n]);
        FOR i:=1 TO (n-1) DO read(manstart,x[i])
    END ELSE
    FOR i:=1 TO n DO read(manstart,x[i])
  END;
  k:= 0;
  WHILE k>=0 DO
  BEGIN
    evalcnt:= 0;  obj(x,0,0,u); IF done THEN GOTO 999;
      showval;
    writeln('Insert -ve no. to start optimization');
    writeln('or zero for no more changes,');
    writeln(' or 1 to ',n:2,' showing value to alter');
```

Continued overleaf

```
    readln(k);
    WHILE (k>0) AND (k<=n) DO
    BEGIN  writeln('Insert new value for x[',k:2,']');
      readln(x[k]);  showval;
      writeln('Insert again - zero or neg to terminate');
      readln(k)
    END;
END;
    {This loop controlled by "k" allows manual alteration
    of values}

maxreach:= 1;
FOR i:= 1 TO n DO step[i]:= 0.1;
FOR i:= 1 TO n DO FOR j:= 1 TO n DO
  IF i=j THEN dir[i, j]:= 1
  ELSE  dir[i, j]:= 0;
  {"dir" is initially set to a unit matrix}
examine;
  {Initial conditions have been set up, and now the
  Rosenbrock optimization begins}
FOR stage:= 1 TO nstages DO
BEGIN trial:= 0;
  origin;
  endstage:= false;
  WHILE NOT endstage DO
  BEGIN  IF fixa THEN effvars:=maxreach ELSE
      effvars:= maxreach+1;
      {"maxreach" is distance reached in trajectory,
      "effvars" is no. of effective variables}
    FOR i:= 1 TO effvars DO
    BEGIN  trial:= trial+1;
      FOR j:= 1 TO n DO
                 xl[j]:= x[j]+step[i]*dir[i, j];
      obj(xl,stage,trial,ul); IF done THEN GOTO 999;
      k:= ul.reach;
      publish:=(evalcnt=1) OR ((evalcnt MOD recordint)=0)
        OR (ul.success AND NOT u.success);
        IF reorigin AND (ul.success AND NOT u.success)
                                          THEN origin;
      IF (k<16) AND (ul.miss = 0) THEN k:= k+1;
      IF k>maxreach THEN
      BEGIN  maxreach:= k; publish:= true;
```

Continued opposite

```
        IF reorigin THEN origin END;
      IF interact THEN examine;
        {"interact" may be set by procedure "obj",
        representing "eval"}
      IF gteq(ul,u) THEN
      BEGIN   succ[i]:= true;  u:= ul;
        FOR j:= 1 TO n DO x[j]:= xl[j];
        prog[i]:= prog[i]+step[i];
        step[i]:= alpha*step[i]
      END ELSE
      BEGIN   fail[i]:= true;
        step[i]:= -beta*step[i]
      END;
      endstage:= maxreach>0;
      FOR j:= 1 TO effvars DO
      IF NOT (succ[j] AND fail[j]) THEN
                                endstage:= false;
      IF guillotine AND (trial >= maxstage) THEN
                 endstage:= true;
      IF endstage THEN publish:= true;
      IF publish THEN stow;
      IF endstage THEN GOTO 1
    END;
  1: END;
  orth(prog, dir, b1, b2, effvars);
  IF NOT repoint THEN
    FOR i:= 1 TO n DO FOR j:= 1 TO n DO
      IF i=j THEN dir[i, j]:= 1
      ELSE  dir[i, j]:= 0;
    {If "repoint" is false, "dir" is made unit vector}
  writeln(results,'Stage', stage:3, ' Trials', trial:5,
        ' Evalns', evalcnt:5);
  writeln(results,'Progress in stage', b1:9);
  writeln(results,'Ratio 1st 2 compts', b2/b1:9);
  writeln(results,'Objective fn.', u.reach:3, u.miss:7,
                                          u.tim:7);
  writeln(results,'Variables:');
  FOR j:= 1 TO n DO
  IF (j MOD 6 = 0) OR (j=n) THEN writeln(results,x[j]:9)
      ELSE write(results,x[j]:9);
  writeln(results)
END {of stage};
```

Continued overleaf

```pascal
   999: IF NOT endstage THEN stow;   obj(x,-1,-1,u);
END {rose};

BEGIN   alpha:= 3;   beta:= 0.5;
   done:= false;
   writeln('Insert damping factor');   readln(b);
   writeln('Insert evalint');   readln(evalint);
   guillotine:= ask('Guillotine stage? Y/N');
   IF guillotine THEN BEGIN
      writeln('Insert maxstage');   readln(maxstage);
   END;
   repoint:= ask('Reassign directions? Y/N');
   fixa:= ask('Keep a fixed? Y/N');
   reorigin:=ask('Reoriginate prog. and succ/fail? Y/N');
   display:= true;   evalcnt:= 0;
   writeln('Name of file for running results?');
   readln(filename);
   assign(results, filename);   rewrite(results);
   writeln('Insert recording interval');   readln(recordint);
   filestart:= ask('Start from filed values? Y/N');
   IF filestart THEN
BEGIN   writeln('Name of file for starting values?');
      readln(filename);   assign(manstart, filename);
      reset(manstart);
END;
   writeln(results,'Damp factor ',b:5,
                      '    Recordint ',recordint:5);
   IF filestart THEN writeln(results,'Start from file ',
                                              filename)
       ELSE writeln(results,'Not file start');
   IF reorigin THEN writeln(results,'With reorigination');
   IF guillotine THEN writeln(results,'Guillotine at ',
                                           maxstage:5)
       ELSE writeln(results,'No guillotine');
   IF repoint THEN writeln(results,
                               'Reassignment of directions')
       ELSE writeln(results,'No reassignment of directions');
   IF fixa THEN writeln(results,'Fixed acceleration value')
       ELSE writeln(results,'Acceleration value variable');
   writeln(results);
   rose(17, 2000, eval);   {Call of procedure "rose"}
   END.
```

The evaluation procedure, inserted from the file B:SIXEVAL.PAS, is as follows. The name SIXEVAL is carried over from an earlier program called *sixteen* which simulated the trajectory in sixteen segments, as described in the text. When the program was adapted to become PROCEDURE *eval*, the name formed by combining *sixteen* and *eval* was shortened to SIXEVAL.

The procedure incorporates a PROCEDURE *display*, which generates a pictorial representation of the trajectory in a form that requires only text output. In an earlier version of the program, written in Turbo Pascal to run on an IBM PC, a true graphics display was used, but this one can run on a system without graphics capabilities. In Turbo Pascal the arrangement of the overall program had to be slightly modified because Turbo Pascal does not allow procedural parameters to procedures.

```
PROCEDURE eval(v: vec; stage,trial: integer; VAR ev:evaln);

LABEL 1, 999;

VAR   a, intercept: real;   i,j,reached: integer;
      failed: boolean;
      theta, x, y, xd, yd, t: ARRAY[0..16] OF real;
      {"theta" is the set of control angles, stored as
      tangents. "x", "y", "t" are coordinates and times at
      boundaries of segments, and "xd", "yd" refer to
      time derivatives}
      hit: ARRAY[1..4] OF boolean;

PROCEDURE solve(x, a, b, k1, k2: real;   VAR t: real);
   {This evaluates the time "t" by successive approximation,
   as required where damping coeff. "b" is non-zero}
   VAR  cnt: integer;   tlo, thi, ttry, xx: real;
   FUNCTION  evl(t:real):real;
   BEGIN  evl:= a*t/b + k1*exp(-b*t) + k2  END {evl};
   BEGIN  tlo:=0;  thi:=0.1;  xx:= evl(thi);
      WHILE (xx<x) AND (thi<100) DO
      BEGIN  thi:= 2*thi;  xx:= evl(thi)  END;
      IF thi>=100 THEN
      BEGIN  failed:= true;  GOTO 1  END;
      ttry:= (tlo+thi)/2;
```

Continued overleaf

```
    FOR cnt:= 1 TO 10 DO
    BEGIN  xx:= evl(ttry);
      IF xx<x THEN tlo:=ttry ELSE thi:=ttry;
      ttry:= (tlo+thi)/2
    END;
    t:= ttry
  END {solve};

PROCEDURE step(posn:integer);
  {simulates movement of particle through one of
                                    16 segments}
  VAR  xxd,yyd,xxdd,yydd,tt,k1,k2,t1,t2,disc:real;
  BEGIN  xxdd:= a/sqrt(1+sqr(theta[posn]));
         yydd:= a*theta[posn]/sqrt(1+sqr(theta[posn]));
         xxd:= xd[posn-1];  yyd:= yd[posn-1];
    IF b=0 THEN
    BEGIN  disc:= 4*sqr(xxd) + 2*xxdd;
        IF disc<0 THEN BEGIN failed:=true; GOTO 1 END;
        t1:= (sqrt(disc) - 2*xxd)/(2*xxdd);
        t2:= -(sqrt(disc) + 2*xxd)/(2*xxdd);
        IF t1<0 THEN tt:= t2 ELSE IF t2<0 THEN tt:= t1
          ELSE IF t1<t2 THEN tt:= t1 ELSE tt:= t2;
      t[posn]:= t[posn-1] + tt;
      xd[posn]:= xxd + xxdd*tt;
      yd[posn]:= yyd + yydd*tt;
      y[posn]:= y[posn-1] + yyd*tt + sqr(tt)*yydd/2
    END
    ELSE BEGIN  k1:= (xxdd/b - xxd)/b;  k2:= -k1;
      solve(1/4, xxdd, b, k1, k2, tt);
      t[posn]:= t[posn-1] + tt;
      xd[posn]:= xxdd/b - k1*b*exp(-b*tt);
      k1:= (yydd/b - yyd)/b;  k2:= -k1;
      y[posn]:= y[posn-1] + yydd*tt/b + k1*exp(-b*tt) + k2;
      yd[posn]:= yydd/b - k1*b*exp(-b*tt);
    END;  reached:= posn;
  END {step};

PROCEDURE run;
  {Concatenates "steps" for trajectory}
  VAR cnt:integer;
  BEGIN  FOR cnt:= 1 TO 16 DO
    BEGIN  step(cnt);
```

Continued opposite

```
       IF (cnt=4) AND (y[4]>0) THEN
       BEGIN  hit[1]:= true; intercept:=y[4];
         GOTO 1  END
       ELSE IF (cnt=8) AND (y[8]<1) THEN
       BEGIN  hit[2]:= true; intercept:= 1-y[8];
         GOTO 1  END
       ELSE IF (cnt=12) AND (y[12]>0) THEN
       BEGIN  hit[3]:= true; intercept:=y[12];
         GOTO 1  END
       ELSE IF (cnt=16) AND (y[16]<1) THEN
       BEGIN  hit[4]:= true; intercept:= 1-y[16];
         GOTO 1  END
     END
  END{run};

PROCEDURE show;
  VAR i,j: integer;  ch: char;
    scr: ARRAY[-11..11,0..16] OF char;
  BEGIN
    FOR i:=-11 TO 11 DO FOR j:=0 TO 16 DO
    BEGIN  ch:= ' ';  IF i=0 THEN ch:='-'
      ELSE IF j=0 THEN ch:= '¦'
      ELSE IF (((j=4) OR (j=12)) AND (i>0))
           OR (((j=8) OR (j=16)) AND (i<5))
           THEN ch:='+';
      scr[i,j]:= ch
    END;
    FOR j:= 1 TO reached DO
    BEGIN  i:= round(5*y[j]);
      IF (i > -12) AND (i < 12) THEN scr[i,j]:= 'x'
    END;
    IF stage >= 0 THEN BEGIN
    writeln(output);
    writeln('Evalno.',evalcnt:5,'   Stage', stage:4,
                      '   Trial', trial:4);
    write('Score', reached:3, intercept:7,t[reached]:7);
    FOR i:=11 DOWNTO -11 DO
    BEGIN  writeln(output);
      FOR j:= 0 TO 16 DO write(scr[i,j]:2)
    END END ELSE
    BEGIN
    writeln(results);
```

Continued overleaf

```
      writeln(results,'Final trajectory');
      write(results,'Score', reached:3, intercept:7,
                                        t[reached]:7);
    FOR i:=11 DOWNTO -11 DO
    BEGIN  writeln(results);
      FOR j:= 0 TO 16 DO write(results,scr[i,j]:2)
    END END
END {show};

PROCEDURE query;
  VAR ch: char;
  BEGIN  ch:= ' ';
    WHILE NOT ((ch='Y') OR (ch='y') OR
                     (ch='N') OR (ch='n')) DO
    BEGIN  write('  Continue? Y/N'  ); readln(ch);
      IF (ch='N') OR (ch='n') THEN
      BEGIN done:= true; GOTO 999 END
    END;
    ch:= ' ';  interact:= false;
    WHILE NOT ((ch='Y') OR (ch='y') OR
        (ch='N') OR (ch='n') OR (evalcnt = 1)) DO
    BEGIN  writeln('Interact? Y/N'); readln(ch);
      interact:= (ch='Y') OR (ch='y')
    END;
  END {query};

BEGIN  y[0]:= 0;  xd[0]:= 0;  yd[0]:= 0;  t[0]:= 0;
  FOR i:= 0 TO 16 DO x[i]:= i/4;
  failed:= false;  reached:= 0;
  intercept:= 0;
  a:= v[1];  FOR i:= 1 TO 16 DO theta[i]:= v[i+1];
  IF fixa THEN BEGIN
    a:= v[17];  FOR i:= 1 TO 16 DO theta[i]:= v[i];
  END;
  FOR i:= 1 TO 4 DO hit[i]:= false;
  IF a<=0 THEN BEGIN failed:=true;  GOTO 1 END;
    {This test ensures that "run" is not attempted if "a"
    is not positive.  In the version used with "rosdual" an
    extra test was added such that "run" was similarly not
    attempted if any "theta" value was >100}
  run;  reached:= 16;
```

Continued opposite

```
1: ev.reach:= reached;  ev.miss:= intercept;
      ev.tim:= t[reached];
      ev.success:= (reached=16) AND (intercept=0);
   IF (evalcnt MOD evalint) = 0 THEN
   BEGIN dispmem:=display;  display:= true END;
   IF display OR (stage<0) THEN show;  evalcnt:=evalcnt+1;
   interact:= false;
   IF (evalcnt MOD evalint) = 1 THEN
   BEGIN display:=dispmem;  query END;
   {This somewhat complicated arrangement ensures that
   "display" is called if "evalcnt" holds a multiple of
   "evalint", but a "standing order" for display is
   maintained by "dispmem"}
999: END {eval};
```

A.2 ROSDERIV

The modified program is as follows:

```
PROGRAM rosenbrock(input, output);

CONST  pi= 3.14159265359;

TYPE vec= ARRAY[1..17] OF real;
     mat= ARRAY[1..17,1..17] OF real;
     evaln= RECORD  reach: integer;
                    miss: real;
                    tim: real;
                    success: boolean  END;
```

Continued overleaf

```
VAR   alpha, beta, b: real;
      display, dispmem, interact, publish,
        guillotine, repoint, fixa, filestart,
        derivgoal, timederiv, fiddledir,
        reorigin, done: boolean;
          {Additional booleans are
          "derivgoal" for derivative form of obj. fn.,
          "timederiv" for dy/dt (as yd),
                               not dy/dx (as yd/xd),
          "fiddledir" for initial mod. of "dir"}
      evalcnt, evalint, maxreach, effvars,
        recordint, maxstage,
        derivcnt, maxderivcnt: integer;
          {"derivcnt" is count of evaluations while
          "derivgoal" is true,
          "maxderivcnt" is limit of "derivcnt"}
      filename: string;
      results, manstart: text;

FUNCTION gteq(x, y: evaln): boolean;
BEGIN  IF x.reach <> y.reach THEN
          gteq:= x.reach > y.reach
  ELSE IF x.miss <> y.miss THEN
          gteq:= x.miss < y.miss
  ELSE  gteq:= x.tim <= y.tim
END {gteq};

FUNCTION ask(prompt:string): boolean;
VAR ch: char;
BEGIN  ch:=' ';  WHILE NOT ((ch='Y') OR (ch='y')
  OR (ch='N') OR (ch='n')) DO
  BEGIN writeln(prompt);  readln(ch);
    ask:= (ch='Y') OR (ch ='y')
  END
END {ask};

PROCEDURE orth(prog: vec;  VAR dir: mat;
                    VAR b1, b2: real;  n: integer);
VAR  a: mat;
     i, ii, j: integer;
     x: real;
```

Continued opposite

```
BEGIN   FOR i:= 1 TO n DO   FOR j:= 1 TO n DO
                                      a[i, j]:= 0;
  FOR j:= 1 TO n DO a[n, j]:= prog[n]*dir[n, j];
  FOR i:= n-1 DOWNTO 1 DO   FOR j:= 1 TO n DO
    a[i, j]:= a[i+1, j] + prog[i]*dir[i, j];
  FOR i:= 1 TO n DO
  BEGIN   FOR j:= 1 TO n DO dir[i, j]:= a[i, j];
    FOR ii:= 1 TO i-1 DO
    BEGIN   x:= 0;
      FOR j:= 1 TO n DO x:= x+a[i, j]*dir[ii, j];
      FOR j:= 1 TO n DO
            dir[i, j]:= dir[i, j]-x*dir[ii, j]
    END;
    x:= 0;
    FOR j:= 1 TO n DO x:= x+sqr(dir[i, j]);
    x:= sqrt(x);
    FOR j:= 1 TO n DO dir[i, j]:= dir[i, j]/x
  END;
  x:= 0;   FOR j:= 1 TO n DO x:= x+sqr(a[1, j]);
  b1:= sqrt(x);
  x:= 0;   FOR j:= 1 TO n DO x:= x+sqr(a[2, j]);
  b2:= sqrt(x)
END {orth};

{$I B:DERIVEVA.PAS}

PROCEDURE rose(n, nstages: integer;
        PROCEDURE obj(x: vec; st,tr: integer; VAR u:evaln));
LABEL 1, 999;
VAR  x, x1, step, prog: vec;
     dir: mat;
     succ, fail: ARRAY[1..17] OF boolean;
     i, j, k, stage, trial: integer;
     b1, b2: real;
     u, u1: evaln;
     endstage: boolean;

PROCEDURE origin;
  VAR i: integer;
  BEGIN   FOR i:=1 TO n DO
    BEGIN   prog[i]:= 0;  succ[i]:= false;  fail[i]:= false
    END    END {origin};
```

Continued overleaf

```pascal
PROCEDURE showval;
VAR i: integer;
  BEGIN  writeln(output);  writeln(output);
     FOR i:=1 TO n DO
     BEGIN  write('(',i:2,') ',x[i]:7);
       IF (i=n) OR ((i MOD 5)=0) THEN writeln(output)
          ELSE write(' ')
     END;  writeln(output)
END {showval};

PROCEDURE stow;
VAR i, j: integer;
BEGIN
  writeln(results,'Stage', stage:3, ' Trials', trial:5,
             ' Evalns.', evalcnt:5);
  write(results,'Objective fn.', u.reach:3, u.miss:5,
                                        u.tim:5);
  IF derivgoal THEN writeln(results,' *') ELSE
                                     writeln(results);
     writeln(results,'Variables:');
     FOR j:= 1 TO n DO
     IF (j MOD 6 = 0) OR (j=n) THEN
                               writeln(results,x[j]:9)
       ELSE write(results,x[j]:9);
     writeln(results)
END {stow};

{$I B:EXAMINE.PAS}

BEGIN
  FOR i:= 1 TO n DO x[i]:= 0;
  IF fixa THEN x[n]:=1 ELSE x[1]:=1;
  IF filestart THEN
  BEGIN  IF fixa THEN
    BEGIN read(manstart,x[n]);
      FOR i:=1 TO (n-1) DO read(manstart,x[i])
    END ELSE
    FOR i:=1 TO n DO read(manstart,x[i])
  END;
  k:= 0;
  WHILE k>=0 DO
  BEGIN
```

Continued opposite

```
      evalcnt:= 0;   obj(x,0,0,u);   IF done THEN GOTO 999;
      showval;
      writeln('Insert -ve no. to start optimization');
      writeln('or zero for no more changes,');
      writeln(' or 1 to ',n:2,' showing value to alter');
      readln(k);
      WHILE (k>0) AND (k<=n) DO
      BEGIN  writeln('Insert new value for x[',k:2,']');
        readln(x[k]);   showval;
        writeln('Insert again - zero or neg to terminate');
        readln(k)
      END;
   END;


  maxreach:=1;
  FOR i:= 1 TO n DO step[i]:= 0.1;
  FOR i:= 1 TO n DO FOR j:= 1 TO n DO
    IF i=j THEN dir[i, j]:= 1
    ELSE  dir[i, j]:= 0;
  IF fiddledir THEN BEGIN
  IF fixa THEN
  BEGIN  dir[1,1]:=1/sqrt(2);   dir[1,4]:=1/sqrt(2);
         dir[4,1]:=1/sqrt(2);   dir[4,4]:=-1/sqrt(2)
  END   ELSE
  BEGIN  dir[2,2]:=1/sqrt(2);   dir[2,5]:=1/sqrt(2);
         dir[5,2]:=1/sqrt(2);   dir[5,5]:=-1/sqrt(2)
  END  END;
    {Initial setting of "dir" deviates from unit matrix}
  examine;
  FOR stage:= 1 TO nstages DO
  BEGIN trial:= 0;
    origin;
    endstage:= false;
    WHILE NOT endstage DO
    BEGIN  IF fixa THEN effvars:=maxreach ELSE
        effvars:= maxreach+1;
      FOR i:= 1 TO effvars DO
      IF i<=effvars THEN
      BEGIN  trial:= trial+1;
        FOR j:= 1 TO n DO
                    x1[j]:= x[j]+step[i]*dir[i, j];
          obj(x1,stage,trial,u1);   IF done THEN GOTO 999;
```

Continued overleaf

```
k:= ul.reach;
publish:=(evalcnt=1) OR ((evalcnt MOD recordint)=0)
  OR (ul.success AND NOT u.success);
  IF reorigin AND (ul.success AND NOT u.success)
                                          THEN origin;
IF (k<16) AND (ul.miss = 0) THEN k:= k+1;
IF ((k>maxreach) AND (k>=4)) OR derivgoal THEN
BEGIN  IF NOT derivgoal THEN
  BEGIN publish:= true;  derivgoal:= true;
                                      derivcnt:=0;
    maxreach:= 4*((k-1) DIV 4);
                          IF reorigin THEN origin;
      {Set "derivgoal" and go back to earlier
                                      barrier}
    x:=xl;  obj(x,stage,trial,u);
    IF done THEN GOTO 999;  ul:= u
  END  ELSE
  BEGIN derivcnt:= derivcnt+1;
    IF derivcnt>=maxderivcnt THEN
    BEGIN  publish:=true;  derivgoal:= false;
      IF reorigin THEN origin;
      IF gteq(ul,u) THEN x:= xl;
      obj(x,stage,trial,u);
      IF done THEN GOTO 999;
      ul:= u;  maxreach:= u.reach
    END
  END
END;
IF fixa THEN effvars:=maxreach ELSE
effvars:= maxreach+1;
IF gteq(ul,u) AND (i<=effvars) THEN
BEGIN  succ[i]:= true;  u:= ul;
  FOR j:= 1 TO n DO x[j]:= xl[j];
  prog[i]:= prog[i]+step[i];
  step[i]:= alpha*step[i]
END ELSE
BEGIN  fail[i]:= true;
  step[i]:= -beta*step[i]
END;
IF interact THEN examine;
endstage:= maxreach>0;
FOR j:= 1 TO effvars DO
```

Continued opposite

```
            IF NOT (succ[j] AND fail[j]) THEN
                                 endstage:= false;
            IF guillotine AND (trial >= maxstage) THEN
                      endstage:= true;
            IF endstage THEN publish:= true;
            IF publish THEN stow;
            IF endstage THEN GOTO 1
         END;
       1: END;
       orth(prog, dir, b1, b2, effvars);
       IF NOT repoint THEN
          FOR i:= 1 TO n DO FOR j:= 1 TO n DO
            IF i=j THEN dir[i, j]:= 1
            ELSE  dir[i, j]:= 0;
       writeln(results,'Stage', stage:3, ' Trials', trial:5,
                ' Evalns', evalcnt:5);
       writeln(results,'Progress in stage', b1:9);
       writeln(results,'Ratio 1st 2 compts', b2/b1:9);
       write(results,'Objective fn.', u.reach:3, u.miss:7,
                                             u.tim:7);
       IF derivgoal THEN writeln(results, '   *') ELSE
                                        writeln(results);
       writeln(results,'Variables:');
       FOR j:= 1 TO n DO
       IF (j MOD 6 = 0) OR (j=n) THEN writeln(results,x[j]:9)
          ELSE write(results,x[j]:9);
       writeln(results)
    END {of stage};
    999: IF NOT endstage THEN stow;  obj(x,-1,-1,u);
END {rose};

BEGIN  alpha:= 3;  beta:= 0.5;
   derivgoal:= false;  done:= false;
   writeln('Insert damping factor');  readln(b);
   writeln('Insert evalint');  readln(evalint);
   guillotine:= ask('Guillotine stage? Y/N');
   IF guillotine THEN BEGIN
      writeln('Insert maxstage');  readln(maxstage);
   END;
   repoint:= ask('Reassign directions? Y/N');
   fixa:= ask('Keep a fixed? Y/N');
   reorigin:=ask('Reoriginate prog. and succ/fail? Y/N');
```

Continued overleaf

```
writeln('Insert maxderivcnt');   readln(maxderivcnt);
fiddledir:= ask('Fiddle initial directions?');
timederiv:= ask('Time derivative? Y/N');
display:= true;   evalcnt:= 0;
writeln('Name of file for running results?');
readln(filename);
assign(results, filename);   rewrite(results);
writeln('Insert recording interval');   readln(recordint);
filestart:= ask('Start from filed values? Y/N');
IF filestart THEN
BEGIN   writeln('Name of file for starting values?');
   readln(filename);   assign(manstart, filename);
   reset(manstart);
END;
writeln(results,'Damp factor ',b:5,
                    '   Recordint ',recordint:5);
IF filestart THEN writeln(results,'Start from file ',
                                              filename)
   ELSE writeln(results,'Not file start');
IF reorigin THEN writeln(results,'With reorigination');
IF guillotine THEN writeln(results,'Guillotine at ',
                                        maxstage:5)
   ELSE writeln(results,'No guillotine');
IF repoint THEN writeln(results,
                            'Reassignment of directions')
   ELSE writeln(results,'No reassignment of directions');
IF fixa THEN writeln(results,'Fixed acceleration value')
   ELSE writeln(results,'Acceleration value variable');
IF timederiv THEN writeln(results,'Time derivative');
writeln(results);
rose(17, 2000, eval);
END.
```

The evaluation procedure called in as DERIVEVAL is as follows:

```
PROCEDURE eval(v: vec; stage,trial: integer;
                                        VAR ev:evaln);

LABEL 1, 999;

VAR  a, intercept: real;  i,j,reached: integer;
     failed: boolean;
     theta,x,y,xd,yd,t: ARRAY[0..16] OF real;
     hit: ARRAY[1..4] OF boolean;

PROCEDURE solve(x,a,b,k1,k2:real;  VAR t:real);
  VAR cnt: integer;  tlo, thi, ttry, xx: real;
  FUNCTION  evl(t:real):real;
  BEGIN  evl:= a*t/b + k1*exp(-b*t) + k2  END {evl};
  BEGIN  tlo:=0;  thi:=0.1;  xx:= evl(thi);
    WHILE (xx<x) AND (thi<100) DO
    BEGIN  thi:= 2*thi;  xx:= evl(thi)  END;
    IF thi>=100 THEN
    BEGIN  failed:= true;  GOTO 1  END;
    ttry:= (tlo+thi)/2;
    FOR cnt:= 1 TO 10 DO
    BEGIN  xx:= evl(ttry);
      IF xx<x THEN tlo:=ttry ELSE thi:=ttry;
      ttry:= (tlo+thi)/2
    END;
    t:= ttry
  END {solve};

PROCEDURE step(posn:integer);
  VAR  xxd,yyd,xxdd,yydd,tt,k1,k2,t1,t2,disc:real;
  BEGIN  xxdd:= a/sqrt(1+sqr(theta[posn]));
         yydd:= a*theta[posn]/sqrt(1+sqr(theta[posn]));
         xxd:= xd[posn-1];  yyd:= yd[posn-1];
    IF b=0 THEN
    BEGIN  disc:= 4*sqr(xxd) + 2*xxdd;
        IF disc<0 THEN BEGIN failed:=true; GOTO 1 END;
        t1:= (sqrt(disc) - 2*xxd)/(2*xxdd);
        t2:= -(sqrt(disc) + 2*xxd)/(2*xxdd);
```

Continued overleaf

```
           IF tl<0 THEN tt:= t2 ELSE IF t2<0 THEN tt:= tl
              ELSE IF tl<t2 THEN tt:= tl ELSE tt:= t2;
        t[posn]:= t[posn-1] + tt;
        xd[posn]:= xxd + xxdd*tt;
        yd[posn]:= yyd + yydd*tt;
        y[posn]:= y[posn-1] + yyd*tt + sqr(tt)*yydd/2
      END
   ELSE BEGIN  kl:= (xxdd/b - xxd)/b;   k2:= -kl;
      solve(1/4, xxdd, b, kl, k2, tt);
      t[posn]:= t[posn-1] + tt;
      xd[posn]:= xxdd/b - kl*b*exp(-b*tt);
      kl:= (yydd/b - yyd)/b;   k2:= -kl;
      y[posn]:= y[posn-1] + yydd*tt/b + kl*exp(-b*tt) + k2;
      yd[posn]:= yydd/b - kl*b*exp(-b*tt);
   END;   reached:= posn;
 END {step};


PROCEDURE run;
  VAR cnt:integer;
  BEGIN  FOR cnt:= 1 TO 16 DO
    BEGIN  step(cnt);
      IF (cnt=4) AND (y[4]>0) THEN
      BEGIN  hit[1]:= true; intercept:=y[4];
        GOTO 1  END
      ELSE IF (cnt=8) AND (y[8]<1) THEN
      BEGIN  hit[2]:= true; intercept:= 1-y[8];
        GOTO 1  END                              \
      ELSE IF (cnt=12) AND (y[12]>0) THEN
      BEGIN  hit[3]:= true; intercept:=y[12];
        GOTO 1  END
      ELSE IF (cnt=16) AND (y[16]<1) THEN
      BEGIN  hit[4]:= true; intercept:= 1-y[16];
        GOTO 1  END
    END
  END{run};


PROCEDURE show;
  VAR i,j: integer;  ch: char;
    scr: ARRAY[-11..11,0..16] OF char;
  BEGIN
    FOR i:=-11 TO 11 DO FOR j:=0 TO 16 DO
```

Continued opposite

```
    BEGIN  ch:= ' ';   IF i=0 THEN ch:='-'
      ELSE IF j=0 THEN ch:= '¦'
      ELSE IF (((j=4) OR (j=12)) AND (i>0))
            OR (((j=8) OR (j=16)) AND (i<5))
            THEN ch:='+';
      scr[i,j]:= ch
    END;
  FOR j:= 1 TO reached DO
  BEGIN  i:= round(5*y[j]);
    IF (i > -12) AND (i < 12) THEN scr[i,j]:= 'x'
  END;
  IF stage >= 0 THEN BEGIN
  writeln(output);
  writeln('Evalno.',evalcnt:5,'   Stage', stage:4,
                            ' Trial', trial:4);
  write('Score', ev.reach:3, ev.miss:7,ev.tim:7);
  IF derivgoal THEN write(' *');
    {Asterisk shows that derivative is evaluated}
  FOR i:=11 DOWNTO -11 DO
  BEGIN  writeln(output);
    FOR j:= 0 TO 16 DO write(scr[i,j]:2)
  END END ELSE
  BEGIN
  writeln(results);
  writeln(results,'Final trajectory');
  write(results,'Score', reached:3, intercept:7,
                                  t [reached]:7);

  FOR i:=11 DOWNTO -11 DO
  BEGIN  writeln(results);
    FOR j:= 0 TO 16 DO write(results,scr[i,j]:2)
  END END
END {show};

PROCEDURE query;
  VAR ch: char;
  BEGIN  ch:= ' ';
    WHILE NOT ((ch='Y') OR (ch='y') OR
                    (ch='N') OR (ch='n')) DO
    BEGIN  write('  Continue? Y/N'  ); readln(ch);
      IF (ch='N') OR (ch='n') THEN BEGIN done:=true;
            GOTO 999 END;
    END;
```

Continued overleaf

```
     ch:= ' ';   interact:= false;
   WHILE NOT ((ch='Y') OR (ch='y') OR
       (ch='N') OR (ch='n') OR (evalcnt = 1)) DO
   BEGIN  writeln('Interact? Y/N'); readln(ch);
     interact:= (ch='Y') OR (ch='y')
   END;
  END {query};

BEGIN  IF stage<0 THEN derivgoal:= false;
  y[0]:= 0;  xd[0]:= 0;  yd[0]:= 0;  t[0]:= 0;
  FOR i:= 0 TO 16 DO x[i]:= i/4;
  failed:= false;  reached:= 0;
  intercept:= 0;
  a:= v[1];  FOR i:= 1 TO 16 DO theta[i]:= v[i+1];
  IF fixa THEN BEGIN
    a:= v[17];  FOR i:= 1 TO 16 DO theta[i]:= v[i];
  END;
  FOR i:= 1 TO 4 DO hit[i]:= false;
  IF a<=0 THEN BEGIN failed:=true;  GOTO 1 END;
  run;  reached:= 16;
  1: IF derivgoal AND (reached>maxreach) THEN
     BEGIN  reached:=maxreach;  intercept:=0 END;
     ev.reach:= reached;  ev.miss:= intercept;
       IF derivgoal THEN BEGIN
             IF timederiv THEN BEGIN
             IF odd(maxreach DIV 4) THEN
             ev.tim:=-yd[maxreach] ELSE
             ev.tim:=yd[maxreach] END ELSE BEGIN
             IF odd(maxreach DIV 4) THEN
             ev.tim:=-yd[maxreach]/xd[maxreach] ELSE
             ev.tim:=yd[maxreach]/xd[maxreach] END
          END ELSE
       ev.tim:= t[reached];
          {"ev.tim" depends on "derivgoal" and "timederiv"}
       ev.success:= (reached=16) AND (intercept=0);
  IF (evalcnt MOD evalint) = 0 THEN
  BEGIN dispmem:=display;  display:= true END;
  IF display OR (stage<0) THEN show;  evalcnt:=evalcnt+1;
  interact:= false;
  IF (evalcnt MOD evalint) = 1 THEN
  BEGIN display:=dispmem;  query  END;
999: END {eval};
```

A.3 ROSDUAL

The program for this is as follows. The evaluation procedure introduced is in SIXEVAL, and is exactly as for the original optimization program (except that a small modification, described in a comment statement near the end of SIXEVAL, was found to be necessary).

```
PROGRAM rosenbrock(input, output);

CONST  pi= 3.14159265359;

TYPE vec= ARRAY[1..17] OF real;
     mat= ARRAY[1..17,1..17] OF real;
     evaln= RECORD  reach: integer;
                    miss, tim: real;
                    success: boolean  END;
     snapshot= RECORD count: integer;
                    score: evaln;
                    xvals, stepvals: vec;
                    dirvals: mat  END;
        {This is a snapshot, or dump of relevant variables
        prior to change of goal-type, to allow return}

VAR  alpha, beta, b: real;
     display, dispmem, interact, publish,
        guillotine, repoint, fixa, filestart,
           reorigin, done: boolean;
     evalcnt, evalint, maxreach, effvars,
        recordint, maxstage, maxtry: integer;
           {"maxtry" is number of trials with fixed "a"}
     filename: string;
     results, manstart: text;
     stack: snapshot;
        {This is not really a stack, since with only two
        goal-types it need only allow one entry.  If there
        was deeper nesting of goal-types genuine stacking
        would be needed}
```

Continued overleaf

```
FUNCTION gteq(x, y: evaln): boolean;
BEGIN  IF x.reach <> y.reach THEN
            gteq:= x.reach > y.reach
  ELSE IF x.miss <> y.miss THEN
            gteq:= x.miss < y.miss
  ELSE  gteq:= x.tim <= y.tim
END {gteq};

FUNCTION ask(prompt:string): boolean;
VAR ch: char;
BEGIN  ch:=' ';  WHILE NOT ((ch='Y') OR (ch='y')
  OR (ch='N') OR (ch='n')) DO
  BEGIN writeln(prompt);  readln(ch);
    ask:= (ch='Y') OR (ch ='y')
  END
END {ask};

PROCEDURE orth(prog: vec;  VAR dir: mat;
                    VAR b1, b2: real;  n: integer);
VAR  a: mat;
    i, ii, j: integer;
    x: real;
BEGIN  FOR i:= 1 TO n DO  FOR j:= 1 TO n DO
                                    a[i, j]:= 0;
  FOR j:= 1 TO n DO a[n, j]:= prog[n]*dir[n, j];
  FOR i:= n-1 DOWNTO 1 DO  FOR j:= 1 TO n DO
    a[i, j]:= a[i+1, j] + prog[i]*dir[i, j];
  FOR i:= 1 TO n DO
  BEGIN  FOR j:= 1 TO n DO dir[i, j]:= a[i, j];
    FOR ii:= 1 TO i-1 DO
    BEGIN  x:= 0;
      FOR j:= 1 TO n DO x:= x+a[i, j]*dir[ii, j];
      FOR j:= 1 TO n DO
            dir[i, j]:= dir[i, j]-x*dir[ii, j]
    END;
    x:= 0;
    FOR j:= 1 TO n DO x:= x+sqr(dir[i, j]);
    x:= sqrt(x);
    FOR j:= 1 TO n DO dir[i, j]:= dir[i, j]/x
  END;
  x:= 0;  FOR j:= 1 TO n DO x:= x+sqr(a[1, j]);
  b1:= sqrt(x);
```

Continued opposite

```
  x:= 0;   FOR j:= 1 TO n DO x:= x+sqr(a[2, j]);
  b2:= sqrt(x)
END {orth};

{$I B:SIXEVAL.PAS}

PROCEDURE rose(n, nstages: integer;
      PROCEDURE obj(x: vec; st,tr: integer;
                                    VAR u:evaln));
LABEL 1, 999;
VAR  x, xl, step, prog: vec;
     dir: mat;
     succ, fail: ARRAY[1..17] OF boolean;
     i, j, k, stage, trial: integer;
     bl, b2: real;
     u, ul: evaln;
     endstage: boolean;

PROCEDURE origin;
  VAR i: integer;
  BEGIN  FOR i:=1 TO n DO
    BEGIN  prog[i]:= 0;  succ[i]:= false;  fail[i]:= false
    END    END {origin};

PROCEDURE showval;
VAR i: integer;
  BEGIN  writeln(output);  writeln(output);
      FOR i:=1 TO n DO
      BEGIN  write('(',i:2,') ',x[i]:7);
        IF (i=n) OR ((i MOD 5)=0) THEN writeln(output)
            ELSE write('  ')
      END;  writeln(output)
END {showval};

PROCEDURE stow;
VAR i, j: integer;
BEGIN
  writeln(results,'Stage', stage:3, '  Trials', trial:5,
              '  Evalns.', evalcnt:5);
  writeln(results,'Objective fn.', u.reach:3, u.miss:5,
                                        u.tim:5);

      writeln(results,'Variables: ');
```

Continued overleaf

```
      FOR j:= 1 TO n DO
      IF (j MOD 6 = 0) OR (j=n) THEN writeln(results,x[j]:9)
         ELSE write(results,x[j]:9);
      writeln(results)
END {stow};

{$I B:EXAMINE.PAS}

BEGIN
  FOR i:= 1 TO n DO x[i]:= 0;
  IF fixa THEN x[n]:=1 ELSE x[1]:=1;
  IF filestart THEN
  BEGIN  IF fixa THEN
    BEGIN read(manstart,x[n]);
       FOR i:=1 TO (n-1) DO read(manstart,x[i])
    END ELSE
    FOR i:=1 TO n DO read(manstart,x[i])
  END;
  k:= 0;
  WHILE k>=0 DO
  BEGIN
    evalcnt:= 0;  obj(x,0,0,u); IF done THEN GOTO 999;
    showval;
    writeln('Insert -ve no. to start optimization');
    writeln('or zero for no more changes,');
    writeln(' or 1 to ',n:2,' showing value to alter');
    readln(k);
    WHILE (k>0) AND (k<=n) DO
    BEGIN  writeln('Insert new value for x[',k:2,']');
      readln(x[k]);  showval;
      writeln('Insert again - zero or neg to terminate');
      readln(k)
    END;
  END;

  maxreach:=1;
  FOR i:= 1 TO n DO step[i]:= 0.1;
  FOR i:= 1 TO n DO FOR j:= 1 TO n DO
    IF i=j THEN dir[i, j]:= 1
    ELSE   dir[i, j]:= 0;
  stack.count:=1;  stack.score:= u;
  stack.xvals:= x;  stack.stepvals:= step;
```

Continued opposite

```
stack.dirvals:= dir;
  {This sets up an initial snapshot in "stack"}
examine;
FOR stage:= 1 TO nstages DO
BEGIN trial:= 0;
  origin;
  endstage:= false;
  WHILE NOT endstage DO
  BEGIN  IF fixa THEN effvars:=maxreach ELSE
      effvars:= maxreach+1;
    FOR i:= 1 TO effvars DO
    BEGIN  trial:= trial+1;
    FOR j:= 1 TO n DO
                  xl[j]:= x[j]+step[i]*dir[i, j];
    obj(xl,stage,trial,ul);  IF done THEN GOTO 999;
    k:= ul.reach;
    publish:=(evalcnt=1) OR ((evalcnt MOD recordint)=0)
      OR (ul.success AND NOT u.success);
      IF reorigin AND (ul.success AND NOT u.success)
                                          THEN origin;
    IF (k<16) AND (ul.miss = 0) THEN k:= k+1;
    IF k>maxreach THEN
    BEGIN  maxreach:= k; publish:= true;
      IF reorigin THEN origin END;
    IF interact THEN examine;
    IF gteq(ul,u) THEN
    BEGIN  succ[i]:= true;  u:= ul;
      FOR j:= 1 TO n DO x[j]:= xl[j];
      prog[i]:= prog[i]+step[i];
      step[i]:= alpha*step[i]
    END ELSE
    BEGIN  fail[i]:= true;
      step[i]:= -beta*step[i]
    END;
    IF evalcnt>=(stack.count+maxtry) THEN
    BEGIN  publish:= true;
      IF reorigin THEN
      BEGIN n:=n-1;  origin;  n:=n+1  END;
      IF gteq(u, stack.score) THEN
      BEGIN step[17]:= alpha*step[17];
        stack.xvals:=x;  stack.stepvals:=step;
        stack.score:= u;  stack.count:=evalcnt;
```

Continued overleaf

```
                 stack.dirvals:= dir;
             END   ELSE
             BEGIN   x:= stack.xvals;   step:= stack.stepvals;
                 step[17]:= -beta*step[17];
                 u:= stack.score;   stack.count:=evalcnt;
                 dir:= stack.dirvals;
             END;
             x[17]:= x[17]+step[17];
             IF x[17]<=0 THEN x[17]:=0.01;
         END;
             {The above returns to the "outer" optimization,
             if the condition tested is true}
         endstage:= true;
         FOR j:= 1 TO effvars DO
         IF NOT (succ[j] AND fail[j]) THEN
                                      endstage:= false;
         IF guillotine AND (trial >= maxstage) THEN
                     endstage:= true;
         IF endstage THEN publish:= true;
         IF publish THEN stow;
         IF endstage THEN GOTO 1
     END;
  1: END;
  orth(prog, dir, b1, b2, effvars);
  IF NOT repoint THEN
     FOR i:= 1 TO n DO FOR j:= 1 TO n DO
         IF i=j THEN dir[i, j]:= 1
         ELSE   dir[i, j]:= 0;
  writeln(results,'Stage', stage:3, ' Trials', trial:5,
           ' Evalns.', evalcnt:5);
  writeln(results,'Progress in stage', b1:9);
  writeln(results,'Ratio 1st 2 compts', b2/b1:9);
  writeln(results,'Objective fn.', u.reach:3, u.miss:7,
                                          u.tim:7);
  writeln('Variables:');
  FOR j:= 1 TO n DO
  IF (j MOD 6 = 0) OR (j=n) THEN writeln(results,x[j]:9)
     ELSE write(results,x[j]:9);
  writeln(results)
  END {of stage};
  999: IF NOT endstage THEN stow;  obj(x,-1,-1,u);
END {rose};
```

Continued opposite

```
BEGIN  alpha:= 3;   beta:= 0.5;
  done:= false;
  writeln('Insert damping factor');   readln(b);
  writeln('Insert evalint');   readln(evalint);
  guillotine:= ask('Guillotine stage? Y/N');
  IF guillotine THEN BEGIN
    writeln('Insert maxstage');   readln(maxstage);
  END;
  writeln('Insert max try at one goal');   readln(maxtry);
  repoint:= ask('Reassign directions? Y/N');
  fixa:= true;
  reorigin:=ask('Reoriginate prog. and succ/fail? Y/N');
  display:= true;   evalcnt:= 0;
  writeln('Name of file for running results?');
  readln(filename);
  assign(results, filename);   rewrite(results);
  writeln('Insert recording interval');   readln(recordint);
  filestart:= ask('Start from filed values? Y/N');
  IF filestart THEN
  BEGIN  writeln('Name of file for starting values?');
    readln(filename);   assign(manstart, filename);
    reset(manstart);
  END;
  writeln(results,'Damp factor ',b:5,
                    ' Recordint ',recordint:5);
  writeln(results,'Maxtry',maxtry:5);
  IF filestart THEN writeln(results,'Start from file ',
                                              filename)
    ELSE writeln(results,'Not file start');
  IF reorigin THEN writeln(results,'With reorigination');
  IF guillotine THEN writeln(results,'Guillotine at ',
                                              maxstage:5)
    ELSE writeln(results,'No guillotine');
  IF repoint THEN writeln(results,
                            'Reassignment of directions')
    ELSE writeln(results,'No reassignment of directions');
  IF fixa THEN writeln(results,'Fixed acceleration value')
    ELSE writeln(results,'Acceleration value variable');
  writeln(results);
  rose(17, 2000, eval);
  END.
```

Appendix B The Gram-Schmidt Method

B.1 THE METHOD

The method is described by Birkhoff and MacLane (1953), Rosenbrock (1960), Schwefel (1981) and others. Explanatory comments have been inserted in the first appearance of **procedure** *orth* in Appendix A.

The method operates on a set of n vectors, in n-space, which must be *independent*, in the usual mathematical sense. It derives from them a set forming a *normal orthogonal basis*.

Rosenbrock's implementation starts from an earlier *normal orthogonal basis* and derives the new one whose first component is aligned with the vector representing the overall advance in the previous stage. It starts by forming in matrix a a set of n vectors, of which that in the first row corresponds to the overall advance of the previous stage. This is done by filling the n-th row of a with a vector representing the component of the previous advance that was along the previous n-th direction, the $(n-1)$-th row with the summed progress for the n and $(n-1)$-th previous directions, and so on until the first row holds a vector representing the total progress in the stage.

The r-th row of a comes to hold the summed progress along a subset of directions of the previous *normal orthogonal basis*, from that numbered r to that numbered n. It is easy to show that a holds a set of n independent vectors, provided the progress along each of the previous directions was non-zero. This is the starting point for the Gram-Schmidt method as such.

The method establishes the first vector of its new basis by copying the first row of a into the first row of *dir*, and simply scaling it to become a unit vector. For the subsequent vectors, the appropriate row of a (the r-th, say) is copied into *dir*, but before it is scaled to become a unit vector it has subtracted from it its own orthogonal projection onto each of the $(r-1)$ unit vectors already computed. The magnitude of the projection is computed as the *dot*, or *inner product* of the new vector in row r with the unit one in the earlier row, and the vector projection to be subtracted is the unit vector times this magnitude.

The method is described and justified more formally by Birkhoff and MacLane. It can be seen that it produces a set of mutually orthogonal unit vectors, provided the adjustment by subtracting projections on earlier rows does not cause a vector to collapse to zero. This will happen if the initial set of n vectors is not independent.

Index

AM (Lenat) 74
analog computing 25, 66, 93
analogy 7, 66
ARCHES 70
associative net 85
automaton theory 63

backpropagation (≡ vector significance feedback) 49
backtracking 15, 124
backvisiting 124
basic learning heuristic 7, 67
Beagle 67, 71
belief network 61
brachistochrone 95
bug-detectors 77

calculus of variations 95
catastrophe theory 12
cell assembly 89
cerebellum 84, 85
cerebral hemispheres 93
checker playing 5, 18, 40, 44
chess 65
combinatorial explosion 15
computational demons 9
computational depth 61
concept-niche 76
concept of a concept 12, 76, 81, 99
conditional jumps 5
conditional probability computer 27
conditioned reflex 26
conjugation (in *pandemonium*) 45
conservation (Piaget) 74
continuity 7

correlation 31
credit assignment 47

Daisyworld 52, 87
dynamic programming 95

earthworms 76
edibility (concept) 86
effective fluctuations 36
elementary exemplification 19, 82
error decorrelation 39
error-information 36
EURISKO 74
evolution 10, 52, 71, 76, 81, 88
evolutionary programming 71
expert system 2
extrapolation 7
extreme case heuristic 74

finite automaton 6, 63, 71
fuzzy set theory 21, 30, 70

hedony 35, 86
heuristic 14, 91, 96, 122
heuristic connection 7, 66
hidden unit 8
hierarchical structure 119
hill-climbing 37
homunculus 83
Hopfield net 58, 67

impasse 1
induction 15, 37
interpolation 7

Janet   46
jokes   72, 122
Kalman filter   17, 42
key point   50, 102

language   72, 76, 122
lateral thinking   29
learning   3, 5
learning automaton   16
learning filter   17, 35, 42
least commitment   88
logic, two senses of term   9

manual adjustment   119
mapping   83
means-ends analysis   14, 82, 107, 124
mesa phenomenon   8, 113
meta-goal   79
microelectrode   3
minimum-time path   95
missionaries and cannibals problem   29
model   11, 38, 78, 80
model neuron   4, 58
motor control   10, 13, 76, 83, 91
mutated fission   9, 45, 67

near miss   93
nerve impulse   57
neural net   4, 56
neural plasticity   84
nonmonotonic reasoning   21, 28
non-parametric statistics   31

Occam's razor   78
odd and even objective functions   35
optimization   106, 112, 141
orthogonalization   39, 111, 116, 124, 172

paleo-AI   125
pandemonium   8, 45, 67
parallel distributed processing   47
parametric statistics   31
path control   94, 96
pattern classification   33, 41
perceptron   41, 60
performance program   16
physics   19, 122
piano-mover's problem   95, 96
plausible reasoning   15
Pontryagin method   95
potential field   97
probability   21, 27
process control   34
prototypicality   72

quasi-continuity   8

ratiocination   9
regression   2
resolution method   17
reticular formation   89
robotics   13, 91, 122
Rosenbrock optimization   98, 106, 110

salience   72
self-organization   6, 43
set theory   65, 122
shaggy dog story   74
significance feedback   46
simulation   104
skill acquisition   93
sodium pump   56
sofa problem   95, 96
space war   26
state-determined system   63
strong AI position   1
succinctness   78
system   63

tail-flicks   86, 99

teleology   79

teraphim   3

toy problem   103, 122

uncertainty   21

wandering correlator   50

way point   102

worth   46